CW00693077

Theory and Practice of Contrast

Theory and Practice
of Contrast
Integrating Science, Art and Philosophy

Mariusz Stanowski

CRC Press
Taylor & Francis Group
Boca Raton London New York

CRC Press is an imprint of the
Taylor & Francis Group, an **informa** business

First edition published 2021
by CRC Press
6000 Broken Sound Parkway NW, Suite 300, Boca Raton, FL 33487-2742

and by CRC Press
2 Park Square, Milton Park, Abingdon, Oxon, OX14 4RN

CRC Press is an imprint of Taylor & Francis Group, LLC

ISBN: 978-0-367-77002-0 (hbk)
ISBN: 978-0-367-77439-4 (pbk)
ISBN: 978-1-003-17138-6 (ebk)

Typeset in Times
by Deanta Global Publishing Services, Chennai, India

Contents

Foreword

The book *Theory and Practice of Contrast: Integrating Science, Art and Philosophy* is situated at the intersections between several disciplines, including cognitive science, theory of information/complexity, physics, philosophy and art. Contrast as a method has proven value in all kinds of sciences as it constitutes the basic and most important type of reasoning. In linguistics and semiotics, for example, it refers to a relation between two compatible units in the form of "x and y". By extension, contrast implies opposition—a relation of type "x or y". While the former introduces combinations, the latter builds upon selections. Contrasts also function as limits or poles, as departing and ending points that have different steps or levels in-between. This is the case of narrative and storytelling in which a character goes from one state of being to another through a series of actions, choices and consequences. Furthermore, at a large scale, contrasts work as an operational method to compare data, facts, contexts, dates and situations. Contrast helps us to relate new knowledge within the framework of previous discoveries and of possible predictable scenarios in the future.

In this work, Mariusz Stanowski, elaborates an interdisciplinary theory of contrast that gives special attention to visual phenomena. Indeed, the reader is guided with a clear language and with diverse concrete examples through the uses and variations of visual contrast. The diversity of topics and the manner in which they are structured are also in itself exercises to apply contrast as a unificatory mechanism. The author reminds us to keep an eye open to perception, cognition, aesthetics and computing with respect to images. This is an appreciated effort because it builds upon the idea that visual reasoning can be abstracted and then adapted to other forms of materiality. I believe this book will open perspectives and will invite the reader to continue the explorations in visual interdisciplinarity.

Everardo Reyes

About the Author

Mariusz Stanowski graduated from Warsaw University of Technology (1974), and Fine Arts Academy in Warsaw (1979), where he worked later as an academic teacher and designer. Currently he is a visual artist and an independent researcher. His scientific research is situated on the borderline between humanities and natural sciences, including: philosophy, art theory, cognitive science, theory of information/complexity and physics. As an artist, through paintings, defined as deconstructed, he tries to express the idea of creativity. He has exhibited in Poland and abroad, including Vikingsberg Museum of Modern Art, (Helsingborg, Sweden), Charlottenborg Palace (Kobenhavn, Danmark), and the Visual Art Museum - School of Visual Arts (New York, USA).

Introduction

One of the reasons that we experience a slowdown in scientific development is the lack of communication between the various fields of knowledge that remain within the individual, narrow specializations. There has been an infirmity as a result of more and more detailed and less relevant research, which no longer concerns reality but rather the existing state of knowledge. Although much has been said about the need for interdisciplinarity, there is still a lack of deep interdisciplinary research on a fundamental scientific level. We are witnessing radical advances in technology, but science still has many important issues to resolve. A lack of understanding of these issues prevents its further development. *Theory and Practice of Contrast* takes a significant step towards understanding these foundations, integrating them and building a coherent image of reality. It combines the fields of science, philosophy and art and explains the issues that were impossible to understand within individual fields. It also proves how much humanities are important for science and vice versa—scientific approach for humanities (its understanding and development)—and what a significant impact it can have on education in both areas.

The content is based on understanding the essence of visual interactions, which reduces to a new definition of contrast. It turns out (which is explained in detail in the book) that the considerations of visual interactions (contrasts) can be generalized to all other interactions that we are familiar with, i.e. to everything (because everything that exists is some kind of interaction). Therefore, this definition of contrast/impact has become a common/integrating element for all, even the most remote areas of knowledge. Thanks to this not only was a deep integration of science possible within existing areas (e.g. humanities), but also the integration of humanities with natural sciences, e.g. aesthetics with information theory, epistemology, ontology and physics. The integration is also a source of understanding/explanation and the development of particular fields, which in turn has an impact on development in general.

The book is written in a simple language (to allow concentration on the content) but requires attention and reasoning as it is a closely related sequence of associations (almost as in mathematics) that must be traced during reading (cursory reading precludes the possibility of understanding, which is crucial here). Also recognizing fundamental/basic issues in the above-mentioned fields is needed, as opposed to having only descriptive or encyclopaedic knowledge about them, which equalizes the level of importance of issues. For example, in art theory (and also in cognitive science), it is necessary to know that we still do not have a general and objective definition of art/beauty and are aware of how it is important. One of the concrete consequences of this lack is the still unresolved mystery of the golden division (a symbol of objective beauty which has intrigued us for 2,500 years). In the theory of information, we should be aware that there is still no general definition of information (just as there is no general definition of complexity) and that the relationship between energy and information is unclear. In physics, we don't have unification of basic forces; we also don't have a confirmed theory of the universe (there are only hypotheses). It is also very important to note that physics examines reality external to our mind, i.e. unilaterally, not including the analysis of our mind, while the observed reality is also significantly influenced by the specifics of the mind. In chemistry, which addresses topics such as how atoms and molecules interact via chemical bonds to form new chemical compounds, the general definition of interaction as a tension (contrast), also resulting from the complexity of the objects interacting, is not considered. In philosophy, there is no explicit definition of fundamental concepts such as beauty, subjectivity, value, cognition and being. This research has been able to link and thus help in understanding much deeper these fundamental concepts and issues. They include, among others:

1. New definition/understanding of contrast as the universal law of nature and principle of being. The book shows, on various examples, the versatility of the definition, how it binds together distant concepts and areas of meaning and how, therefore, it has great explanatory power.
2. Formulating a general definition of complexity (needed and missing today) and reconciling discrepancies in existing definitions. This general definition of complexity proved to be a different formulation of contrast definition (what was a big surprise, as these two seemingly incomparable concepts were unified here).
3. Quantitative and objective explanation of the causes of aesthetic preferences and attractiveness of aesthetic objects, including an explanation of golden division attractiveness.
4. General and objective definition of art (still missing). There has been a surprising identification of beauty with the complexity/compression of information—that is, energy savings when receiving information. It follows that if we have two different objects, but containing the same amount of information (needed for their perception), we will like this object more whose perception requires less energy (effort). The above conclusion explains in a quantitative way such important and fundamental knowledge concepts as beauty, art, goodness, development and value.
5. Finding objective rules of colour combinations. Until today, there is practically no knowledge about the aesthetics of colour combinations. In this book, based on the knowledge of beauty, contrast and complexity, for the first time, the impact of colour combinations is explained.
6. New definition/understanding of being as a contrast, i.e. a tension between common and differentiating features of two objects. This definition explains that contrast is the primary concept in relation to the current concept of being (it explains the concept of being as a contrast between two objects having common and differentiating features).
7. Explanation of most important issues related to the concept of information: definition of information and relationship of information with energy (vague until today).

8. Hypothesis of the universe construction as a binary, ever-increasing number. This hypothesis combines cognitive science, philosophy and physics and may be crucial for development in these fields.

This knowledge could be interesting and useful for three groups of readers:

1. Primarily it is addressed to scientists who are interested in a deeper understanding of fundamentals of science—they are most likely to appreciate the value of this study. It would also be useful for those researchers who are trying to transcend their own areas of research in order to broaden and integrate them with other areas of expertise and to introduce new reference points for existing solutions. Particularly important are references to arts and humanities. It is by entering the more general level of consideration that enables to go beyond the specialized areas (narrow specialized areas from different fields are difficult to relate), which could result in the integration and development of current knowledge.
2. At the educational level—for academic teachers and students to acquire the missing fundamental knowledge.
3. At the popular level—for readers with general knowledge of the topics covered, because they will find here new solutions. It may be particularly interesting for those readers who have tried to understand fundamental, yet unresolved issues such as: the definition of art/beauty and the explanation of reasons for aesthetic preferences; the definitions of information, complexity and value; a deeper understanding of being and reality construction.

1 Beauty—Existing Views

Since the history of reflection about beauty is generally known, we will limit ourselves to recalling its most important stages.

Ancient Greeks were the first to attempt to offer a definition of beauty. In the 5th century, Pythagoreans launched the so-called Great Theory of Beauty, according to which beauty resides in the selection of proportions and proper arrangement of parts; that is, it is based on size, quality, quantity and their interrelationship (Vitruvius 1807). That theory prevailed until the 17th century, and no other theory in the history of aesthetics has had such long-lasting power. Its proponents included Aristotle, Plato, Saint Augustine, Dürer, Poussin and also Leibniz, who wrote: "Music charms us, although its beauty consists only in the agreement of numbers" and "The pleasures which sight finds in proportions are of the same nature; and those caused by the other senses amount to almost the same thing" (Leibniz 1714). Meanwhile, other notions were also being articulated. The Great Theory was criticized for the first time by Plotinus as antiquity was drawing to a close. He claimed that "the beauty of proportions comes not so much from the proportions themselves, but rather from the soul which shines through these proportions" (Plotinus 1991). Doubts emerged regarding the objectivity of beauty (first among the Sophists). Epicharm argued that a dog considers a dog most beautiful and similarly an ox an ox, etc. Socrates set forth the thesis that beauty does not lie in the proportion but in the appropriateness or the correspondence of an object to its purpose and nature. According to this view, even a dung basket may be beautiful because it is good for its purpose and a gold shield ugly because gold is inappropriate for it and makes the shield too heavy. It followed that beauty was relative. In the 4th century Basil the Great conceived the idea that beauty resides in relationship, not only among the parts of the object but between the object and the human sight. This was one of the first attempts to take into account the relationship between the object and the subject. In the 13th century that idea was also mentioned by Thomas Aquinas. Spinoza wrote in 1674 that if our constitution was different, what now appears beautiful to us would seem misshapen and what we now think misshapen we should regard as beautiful. The subjective nature of beauty was also noted by D. Hume (Hume 1896), who wrote: "beauty is no quality in things themselves; it exists merely in the mind which contemplates them; and each mind perceives a different beauty". For Hegel (just as for Plotinus), beauty was "the sensual manifestation of the idea". A momentous event in the 18th-century aesthetic theory was Kant's statement (Kant 1952) that "all judgments about beauty are individual judgements. Beauty is asserted for each object separately and is not derived from general propositions".

In the grand philosophical systems of the first half of the 19th century, beauty remained the principal notion of aesthetics. However, already in the second half of that century, experience (or its synonyms such as affection or emotion) came to the forefront of aesthetics (Tatarkiewicz 1980). Aesthetics turned (largely) into a field of psychology; consequently, it became empirical knowledge, and from the 1860s onwards, i.e. beginning with the works of G. Th. Fechner, experimental in nature. What caused the change whereby beauty as a subject was eliminated from aesthetics and aesthetic experience came to be the chief concern of that discipline? In the first place, it was the realization that beautiful objects have no common features, that they are too diverse; hence, there can be no general theory of beauty, a science of beauty. On the other hand, we can identify common characteristics of what we experience vis-à-vis beautiful objects or, to put it differently, the common features of the aesthetic experience. The psychological approach provided aesthetics with a lot of detailed, factual material, and it has been the ambition of 19th- and 20th-century scholars to subsume that material under a general theory. Yet, while that detailed material was largely indisputable, the same could not be said about the theories that generalized beyond the factual material.

New events in art of the early 20th century caused the interest in beauty and its analysis to significantly weaken. Władysław Tatarkiewiczwrites

> During the 20th century both theorists and artists concluded that beauty is a defective concept and it is not possible to construct its theory. Neither is this property so valuable as believed for centuries. The ability of an artwork to shock the observer is more important than that it delights with its beauty. This shock is achieved not only by beauty, but even through ugliness. Nowadays we like ugliness as much as beauty, wrote Apollinaire. H. Read believed that art should not be coupled with beauty. The word "beautiful" is very rarely found in 20th century texts. Its place has been taken up by the term "aesthetic", which carries less historical baggage.
>
> **(Tatarkiewicz 1980)**

Contemporary aesthetics significantly gave up searching for the essence of beauty and art, also as a result of Wittgenstein's philosophy and the efforts of 20th-century anti-essentialism. At present, philosophical aesthetic investigations are focused mainly on issues peripheral to art, such as aesthetic judgement (Sircello 1968), art criticism (Beardsley 1958), sociological and cultural context (Danto 1964; Welsch 1990) or institutional context (Dickie 1974). Contemporary approaches that are more directly concerned with art, such as Formalism (Zangwill 2001; Scruton 1983; Bell 1958) and Anti-Formalism (Walton 1970; Danto 1981; Curie 1989; Carlson 2000), offer more precise language but contribute little to the traditional investigations focusing on the form-content relationship.

In the end of the 20th and in the 21th century the study of aesthetic preferences continues to be pursued mostly in experimental psychology. Such research however has no coherent character and focuses primarily on the individual factors that affect aesthetic preferences, e.g. colour, brightness, saturation, symmetry, contrast, clarity, style, familiarity, emotional state, knowledge, and understanding (Leder et al. 2004).

Another discipline that studies aesthetic preferences is neuroaesthetics. This is a new field with strong links to experimental psychology, which seeks to explain aesthetic experiences at the neurological level. Semir Zeki is considered to be the founder of this discipline (Zeki 2001). These studies, however, like the other in experimental psychology, do not analyze the complex interactions between perceived objects, which are essential for understanding aesthetic experiences. Neuroaesthetics also erroneously assumes that neurological research is primary to analyses of states of mind. The fact that the material elements of the brain have a longer history does not mean that their (mental) analysis is also primary in relation to the (mental) analysis of beauty. If this were the case then neurological research would appear before any reflections on the subject of beauty. In fact, neurological research, e.g. looking for centres that cause a sense of pleasure, is also based on mental assumptions (e.g. that locating these centres will contribute to solving the mystery of beauty). Studying the material elements of the brain as primary in relation to complex mental structures can also be compared to the analysis of a simple computer program that generates complex structures (simple computer programs are able to generate structures of any complexity). In both cases, such an analysis makes no sense. Without neglecting the significance of neurological research in general, it is difficult to understand how this type of research could explain complex relationships at the level of mental structures.

It is difficult to find in the existing literature a position related to the concept of contrast, which could be treated as a reference to these considerations. We've only found two positions: Alfred North Whitehead's cosmology *Process and Reality* (Whitehead 1978) and the theory of Stephen David Ross, based on it: *The Theory of Art: Inexhaustibility by Contrast* (Ross 1982), to which we will refer in the chapter "Interpretations of Existing Views". If we were to indicate existing positions that are closest to this in terms of the nature of the analyses, they would be those that primarily analyze the objects of perception, i.e. works of art and visual structures, as opposed to those analyzing the subject of perception. These are the following positions:

- Arnheim, R., *Art and Visual Perception: A Psychology of the Creative Eye* (Arnheim 1954).
- Gombrich, E., *The Story of Art* (Gombrich 1950).
- Kandinsky, W., *Point and Line to Plane* (Kandinsky 1947).
- Kepes, G., *Language of Vision* (Kepes 1995).
- Klee, P., *Pedagogical Sketchbook* (Klee 1973).
- Strzemiński, W., *Theory of Vision* (Strzemiński 1974).

These works address many important issues that have to do with visual perception. Nevertheless, they do not provide an answer to the question of what the main cause behind our aesthetic preferences is. The most important and interesting of them is R. Arnheim's work entitled *Art and Visual Perception*. This is a study that combines the disciplines of psychology and art theory to present comprehensive knowledge about perceptual experiences, primarily based on Gestalt psychology. The analyses of factors affecting our perceptions, contained in this work, continue to underpin studies of visual perception today. However, they lack a coherent unifying framework to organize and make sense of perceptions. Likewise, the Gestalt theory of visual perception (which will be discussed later) has ultimately failed to propose an integrated model of perceptual processes (Bruce et al. 2003), forming a field of separate visual phenomena.

REFERENCES

Arnheim, R. 1954/1974. *Art and Visual Perception: A Psychology of the Creative Eye.* Berkeley: University of California Press.

Beardsley, M.C. 1958. *Aesthetics: Problems in Philosophy of Criticism.* New York: Harcourt, Brace and Company, Inc.

Bell, C. 1958. *Art.* New York: Capricorn Books. 28.

Bruce, V., Green, P. & Georgeson, M. 2003. *Visual Perception: Physiology, Psychology and Ecology.* (4th ed.) Psychology Press.

Carlson, A. 2000. *Aesthetics and the Environment, Art and Architecture.* London: Routledge.

Currie, G. 1989. *An Ontology of Art.* Basingstoke: Macmillan.

Danto, A. 1964. The artworld. *Journal of Philosophy* 61(19): 571–584.

Danto, A. 1981. *The Transfiguration of the Commonplace.* Cambridge, MA: Harvard University Press.

Dickie, G. 1974. *Art and the Aesthetics: An Institutional Analysis.* Cornell University Press.

Gombrich, E. 1950. *The Story of Art.* London: Phaidon.

Hume, D. 1896. *A Treatise of Human Nature.* London: Clarendon Press.

Kandinsky, W. 1947. *Point and Line to Plane.* Mineola, New York: Dover Publications.

Kant, I. 1952. *Kritik der urteilskraft* [Critique of Judgment]. Oxford: Clarendon Press.

Kepes, G. 1995. *Language of Vision.* New York: Dover Publications.

Klee, P. 1973. *Pedagogical Sketchbook.* London: Faber & Faber.

Leder, H., Belke, B., Oeberst, A. & Augustin, D. 2004. A model of aesthetic appreciation and aesthetic judgments. *British Journal of Psychology* 95: 489–508.

Leibniz, G. 1714. Principles of nature and of grace based on reason. *Philosophical Papers* 2: 1033–1043.

Plotinus. 1991. *The Enneads.* London: Penguin Books.

Ross, S.D. 1982. *A Theory of Art: Inexhaustibility by Contrast.* New York: State University of New York.

Scruton, R. 1983. *The Aesthetic Understanding.* London: Methuen. 177.

Sircello, G. 1968. Subjectivity and justification in aesthetic judgements. *Journal of Aesthetic and Art Criticism* 2: 3–12.

Strzemiński, W. 1974. *Teoria widzenia* [Theory of Vision]. Warsaw: Wydawnictwo Literackie.

Tatarkiewicz, W. 1980. *A History of Six Ideas. An Essay in Aesthetics.* Boston: Kluwer.

Vitruvius, M.P. 1807. *De Architectura* [The Architecture]. Leipzig: Schneider.

Walton, K. 1970. Categories of art. *The Philosophical Review* 79: 334–367.

Welsch, W. 1990. *Aesthetisches Denken.* Stuttgart: Reclam Verlag.

Whitehead, A.N. 1978. *Process and Reality.* New York: A Division of Macmillan Publishing Co, Inc.

Zangwill, N. 2001. *The Metaphysics of Beauty.* Ithaca: Cornell University Press.

Zeki, S. 2001. Artistic creativity and the brain. *Science* 293(5527): 51–52.

2 The Concept's Origin

The repertoire of 20th-century art embraced elements representing (in a general sense) all realms of our reality, such as ready-made objects, the body, life (as an artwork), the creative process, the Earth, context, institutions, social developments, politics, the environment and science. As Grzegorz Dziamski noted, following Boris Groys (Dziamski 2009):

> Today everything may be art; everything may function as art, because art has liberated itself of all constraints, including the constraints of its own definition, and gained absolute freedom. Art became absolute, as Boris Groys says. It became absolute because it made anti-art a fully legitimate part of itself, and from that moment on, from the time anti-art was incorporated in the realm of art, it is not possible to either undermine or negate art, because even negation of art is art, as attested moreover by a long, almost century-old tradition, going as far back as the first Ready-mades of Marcel Duchamp.

Conceptualism brought the process of the differentiation of these domains to completion by identifying the thought itself (idea, content) with the formal component of art (Kosuth). It considerably expanded not only the range of art form types but also the variety of types of impacts exerted on the observer, which today may be actually unlimited (provided it is not against the law).

Thus, any attempt to discover the common characteristics of aesthetic impacts (broadly understood as also including artistic impacts) today would need to encompass features common to all possible types of impacts. Common features of all impacts are actually the features of impacts in general. Therefore, in order to comprehend the essence of aesthetic impacts, it would be necessary to understand the nature of impacts in general. From my days as a student at the Department of Painting, I remember that a given painting or a fragment of it would not be described as fine or ugly, but rather as striking or failing to have an effect. It took me a while to comprehend the meaning of that expression. When it happened, it was an important discovery for me, which I am going to describe.

It is not easy to realize what affects us visually (e.g. in paintings) because in this area, just like in any other field of study, a lot of practice and experience is required to establish the hierarchy of importance among visual effects. In the case of visual structures, experience can be gained by closely observing and comparing visual objects, by probing what stimuli are pleasing to us, which of them we find interesting and what they have in common. Below a short description of such preliminary inquiries is presented in order to better explain the origin of the proposed framework.

The aim of the analysis was to identify what stimulates us visually in any way. In other words, what attracts our attention, stimulates our interest or appears pleasing to us, and in what way such impacts could be reinforced. The easiest to observe were the simplest phenomena, such as differences in form, colour, texture among distinguishable visual objects. It seemed obvious that if such differences were to be accentuated through, for example, the application of more intensive means, this would result in stronger impacts. Yet, equally strong effects were produced by (equally appealing were) visual structures that exhibited minor differences, such as a range of greyness. It was difficult to explain. Proceeding with the inquiry, we found that among multiple objects that are distinguishable in a painting, some affect (impact) "each other" more strongly, while others less so. Some objects tend to be perceived jointly, while other objects separately. It was surprising to observe that the objects that affect "each other" more strongly are not those that are most different from each other but rather the objects that are perceived jointly, that is, objects that have more numerous/stronger features in common. This led to the realization that it is not possible to perceive any differences (contrasts) between visual objects without such objects being juxtaposed (connected, observed jointly and compared). In other words, common features of these objects must exert some influence. Stronger common features reinforce comparisons between differentiating features and produce stronger attraction between them, consequently making their impact stronger. What we see here is a kind of tension resulting from the impacts of common features and of the features that distinguish perceived objects. This tension (contrast) becomes more pronounced as common, and differentiating features become stronger. Apart from purely visual features such as shape, size and colour, the features of visual objects also include their meanings, such as a hand, a chair or a tree, which may also function as common or differentiating features. A tension arises where the meanings are similar while forms differ, and vice versa: the meanings differ, but forms are alike. This type of tension is frequently found in painting. For example, Picasso employed it deliberately when he gave one hand a completely different form than to the other; Matisse painted symmetrical halves of a face with different colours and Escher designed patterns, in which figures and gaps between them had the same form but different meanings. Another issue that had to be examined was the influence of individual tensions on the entire painting and whether or not they are cumulative. It turned out that yes, they are. The greater is the number of tensions, the stronger the impact of the painting as a whole. It was not yet sufficiently clear, however, why stronger tension is more attractive visually. Is it because split emotions triggered by common and differentiating features stimulate the mind, energize it? In order to answer this question, it proved helpful to realize that in perceiving the contrast between two or more objects, we also experience, besides the impact of differentiating features, the influence of common features that causes contrasting objects to become connected. Such connection may be stronger or weaker, thus creating a new structure (composed of such objects) of varied staying power. The emergence of new structures may be equated, in the general sense, to development, which in the case of visual structures means the development of our imagination.

REFERENCE

Dziamski, G. 2009. *Sztuka po końcu sztuki. Sztuka początku XXI wieku* [Art after End of Art. Art of 21th Century Beginning]. Poznań: Poznań University Press, 7.

3 Analysis of Contrast

3.1 CONCEPTUAL ANALYSIS OF CONTRAST

The starting point for this investigation was the question: what affects us visually in the general and elementary sense? We will now attempt to answer it. It is obvious that for any impact to arise, we must first observe a distinction. If no difference between objects is perceived, there is no impact. For any difference to be noticed, there must be at least two objects and they must be observed jointly (as juxtaposed, compared). If we consider what connects different objects (i.e. objects with differentiating features), we realize that it is their common features, without which no difference can be observed (Figure 3.1). Such difference is more readily perceived and has a greater impact on us, the stronger their common features). One can speak here about a kind of tension arising as a result of the "attraction" exerted towards differentiating features by common features. We call the impact understood in this way as "contrast" in this investigation. Therefore, in answering the question posed earlier, we can say that, *in the general sense, what affects us is contrast or tension resulting from the impacts (effects) of common and differentiating features of objects/structures. Contrast grows stronger as the number/strength of common and differentiating features held by contrasting objects increases.*

> Note: the term "more/stronger" is specified in Section 6.2 (*perceptual analysis of contrast*), where we explain how the number of features and how their strength affects the contrast.

This abstract definition of contrast makes us aware of all types of interactions (what is their essence). Because everything we experience is an interaction (in the broadest sense), the principle of contrast must be regarded as the most general law on which not only our perception of reality is based, but also the reality itself (independent on us). This definition of contrast differs from the existing definitions, which define contrast as follows:

- Merriam Webster Dictionary—contrast (verb): "to compare two people or things, to show how they are different".
- Oxford Dictionary—contrast (noun): "the state of being strikingly different from something else in juxtaposition or close association".
- Trésor de la Langue Française informatisé—contraste: "opposition (contradistinction) between two or more things, emphasized and highlighted by their closeness or a mutual relationship".
- PWN's Dictionary of Polish Language—contrast: "sharp contradiction between two juxtaposed objects, phenomena, etc."

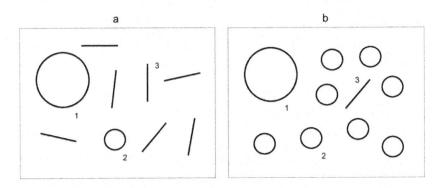

FIGURE 3.1 Influence of the context on impacts of objects. In Figure 3.1a the strongest effects are produced by objects 1 and 2, which have the most features in common, while the same is true of objects 1 and 3 in Figure 3.1b.

How does the proposed definition differ from those cited above?

In the first place, the proposed definition enables to analyze contrast. How? First, contrast is understood here as the impact of varying value (contrast may be stronger or weaker), whereas existing definitions describe contrast as some extreme value: opposition, contradiction or a major distinction.

The second modification is that we take into account common features of contrasting objects, which, just like differentiating features, may differ in terms of impact, power and effect they have on the magnitude of the contrast. Even though the existing general definitions of contrast mention comparisons, juxtapositions and relationships among objects, they do not identify these with common features. For this reason, they fail to explain clearly what the distinction between a contrast and a large difference would consist of.

This ambiguity dissipates once we take into account the impacts of common features and make it clear that, unlike a difference, contrast depends on the power of the latter.

The third change has to do with the nature of contrast being understood as tension resulting from the impacts of common and differentiating features, thus making it possible to analyze contrasts. Although the existing definitions refer to opposition as being emphasized by closeness or mutual relationship, it does not follow that the essence of contrast resides in the tension caused by impacts of common and differentiating features of related objects.

The fourth change is that contrast so far has been understood as a big difference or contradiction, and, in consequence, it took into account only one feature (one quality) of contrasting objects, i.e. the opposition within the same feature (e.g. small-large and light-dark). Our definition of contrast takes into account all features of contrasting objects (all common and differentiating features) and thus takes into account the diversity of objects. It is possible to juxtapose two different qualities, e.g. size (circle) and shape (line), if their common feature is isolation (Figure 3.1). Extracting takes into account the context or features of the object, which can be extracted due to the context, e.g. the size of a large circle in the context of other, smaller elements. Among these elements, one of them may differ (distinguish) by another feature, e.g. colour, then the size with the colour will be compared (i.e. make contrast).

3.2 UNDERSTANDING CONTRAST IN PSYCHOLOGY

An example of not considering the role of common features in contrasts is the understanding of contrast found in Gestalt psychology and also in contemporary studies of perception (Ramachandran and Hirstein 1999), where common (grouping) features are dealt with as separate perceptual characteristics:

> Grouping, as we have already noted, is an important principle, but the extraction of features prior to grouping—which involves discarding redundant information and extracting contrast—is also "reinforcing".

Here the contrast is understood as the separation (extraction) of features. Although it is hardly self-evident, common features must be at work here as well. They make it possible to juxtapose contrasting objects, such as a red figure and green background. In this case the common feature is the "proximity" (superimposition) of the figure and the background. When the figure is moved away, the contrast will become weaker or disappear altogether. Extracting figures from the background is also the fundamental principle of Gestalt psychology (Wertheimer 1923). Note, however, that a contrast between two objects is a more general concept than the contrast defined as extraction (of the figure from its background), because, as was mentioned before, extraction itself is the contrast of two objects, of the figure and the background.

By taking the contrast between two objects (basic contrast) as the basis of all impacts we can also analyze complex structures/objects, such as artworks. The method of analysis consists of identifying and adding up basic contrasts, which makes it possible to approximate, and in some cases, such as golden division, a precise quantitative analysis. As we will see, by applying this method, we are able to explain what determines our aesthetic preferences and gain a better insight into the existing conceptions regarding visual perception.

3.3 COMMON FEATURES AND THE CONTEXT

By means of examples we will see the role played by common features in the contrast. It is believed that the first to describe contrast was the 17th-century philosopher John Locke (Kushner 2008), who observed that tepid water may appear warm or cold depending on whether the hand was immersed before in cold or warm water. What impresses us in that experiment is the fact that the same water seems to have different temperatures. A strong juxtaposition (superimposition) of these differentiating features produces a powerful contrast. Another important factor affecting contrast is the context (other objects) in which the specific contrast is considered. Figure 3.1 shows the influence of context and common features on contrast.

Let us examine Figure 3.1a to see which forms affect each other more strongly: form 1 and form 2 or form 1 and form 3. We find that forms 1 and 2 impact (contrast) each other, while the mutual interaction of forms 1 and 3 is almost imperceptible, despite being more varied. *This is so because it is the common features that are primary factors determining the emergence of a contrast.* To verify this claim, let us list the common and differentiating features of forms 1–2 and 1–3 that can be abstracted in this case.

Common features of forms 1–2:
shape, extraction.
Differentiating features of forms 1–2:
size.
Common features of forms 1–3:
none.
Differentiating features of forms 1–3:
size, extraction.

We find that forms 1–2 have more common features. A very strong common feature of forms 1–2 is that of extraction (i.e. being distinct from the rest), owing to which forms 1 and 2 are strongly compared to each other, thus additionally reinforcing the effect of the difference in size. On the other hand, forms 1–3 lack any common features, resulting in nearly no interaction between the differentiating features.

The opposite situation is depicted in Figure 3.1b. In this case forms 1–3 have stronger common features. Because of this, forms 1 and 3 provide a stronger contrast, whereas the contrast between forms 1 and 2 is weaker and less perceptible.

Common features of forms 1–2: shape.
Differentiating features of forms 1–2: size, extraction.
Common features of forms 1–3: extraction.
Differentiating features of forms 1–3: size, shape.

At first glance, forms 1–2 appear to have stronger common features (shape) than forms 1–3. However, when these forms are juxtaposed as in Figure 3.1b, it is extraction, that is, the characteristic of being distinct from the rest, which is the strongest common feature. That is why forms 1–3 are perceived jointly and create the biggest contrast.

REFERENCES

Ramachandran, V. S. & Hirstein, W. 1999. The science of art. *Journal of consciousness Studies* 6(6–7): 15–51.
Wertheimer, M. 1923. Untersuchungen zur Lehre von der Gestalt, 11. *Psychol. Forsch.* 4: 301–350.
Kushner, L. H. 2008. *Contrast in judgments of mental health.* American University: ProQuest.

4 Analyses of Contrasts in Abstract Visual Structures

4.1 SOME EXAMPLES

Grasping the nature of contrast also provides the key to become aware of what affects us in specific objects. Making use of that key involves, among other things, the awareness that anything we like or that attracts our attention, be it artwork, nature, object or a sentence, must embody a strong contrast. This can be a single contrast or multiple contrasts that need to be found (it is easier to find something if we know what we are looking for) and then investigated for elements/structures participating in such contrasts. The size of a contrast may be estimated by calculating the differentiating and common features of contrasting structures. However, such calculations should be considered as approximations only, because the precise power of attraction of particular features cannot always be determined with precision, as it can be done, e.g. in the case of Golden Section.

Figure 4.1a and b presents the same arrangement of three rectangular forms (1, 2 and 3) with the difference that in Figure 4.1b, form 2 is darker than in Figure 4.1a. Let's count and compare the contrasts in both of them.

Contrasts in Figure 4.1a:

1. A contrast between forms 1 and 2, where comparisons are made between their different thicknesses, thanks to their common orientation.
2. A contrast between forms 2 and 3, where different orientations are compared, thanks to their common thickness.

Since forms 1 and 3 lack any common features, their contrast is weak, despite the fact that they have two differentiating features (orientation and thickness). Let us count features that we can distinguish in this case.

Differentiating features: (1) thickness (forms 1 and 2), (2) thickness (forms 1 and 3), (3) orientation (forms 1 and 3) and (4) orientation (forms 2 and 3).

Common features: (1) thickness (forms 2 and 3) and (2) orientation (forms 1 and 2). There are six features in total.

Figure 4.1 represents the same arrangement of forms 1, 2 and 3, except that form 2 has been darkened.

Contrasts:

1. A contrast between forms 1 and 3. After form 2 has been darkened, forms 1 and 3 gained a new feature in common (brightness) and their thickness and orientation are now strongly juxtaposed.

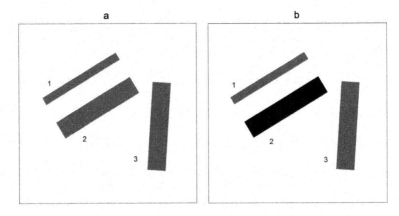

FIGURE 4.1 Comparing contrasts among three rectangular forms of the same length. The forms in Figure 4.1b produce a bigger contrast, which increases their visual attractiveness.

2. A contrast between forms 1 and 2, where their varied thickness and brightness are compared (owing to their common orientation).
3. A contrast between forms 2 and 3, where different orientations and degrees of brightness are compared (due to equal thickness).

Differentiating features: (1) thickness (forms 1 and 2), (2) thickness (forms 1 and 3), (3) orientation (forms 1 and 3), (4) orientation (forms 2 and 3), (5) brightness (forms 1 and 2) and (6) brightness (forms 2 and 3).

Common features: (1) thickness (forms 2 and 3), (2) orientation (forms 1 and 2) and (3) brightness (forms 1 and 3).

There are nine features in total.

The contrast has been considerably reinforced here with three new features. The new structure is characterized by greater complexity, which translates into increased visual attractiveness. The bigger attractiveness of Figure 4.1b can be confirmed here, both visually and mentally, because we see and know that the organization of forms 1, 2 and 3 is here optimal.

Figure 4.2a depicts an arrangement of alternately placed rectangular forms. Contrasts:

1. A contrast of size: the forms have the same shape but are of different size.
2. An illusion of space is also created here, because the smaller elements appear more distant. The juxtaposition of a flat figure with space always creates a contrast.

Differentiating features:

1. Size (bigger and smaller forms).
2. Spatiality (flat figure and illusion of space).

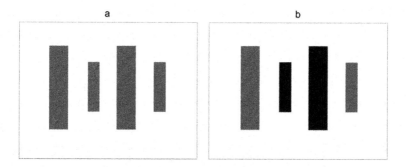

FIGURE 4.2 Contrast of alternating rectangular forms.

Common features:

1. Shape (all elements).
2. Size (elements of the same size).

There are four features in total.

Figure 4.2b represents the same arrangement, except that the centrally placed elements have been darkened.

Contrasts:

1. By darkening the middle elements we additionally gain an illusion of orientation to the left. Large contrast is created because the same middle forms are oriented in two opposite directions simultaneously: towards the right if we concentrate on the sizes of all the elements or towards the left when we focus on the darkened elements.
2. Another large contrast that is obtained by darkening the middle elements consists in the fact that the arrangement has simultaneously an alternating structure (as evidenced by the alternating size of the elements) and a symmetrical structure (as defined by the degrees of brightness). These two mutually contradictory features invite strong comparison because they are superimposed, and superimposition is the strongest common feature.
3. The darkening also intensifies the illusion of space, which increases the contrast with the flatness of the figures.
4. The contrast of size is the same as in Figure 4.2a.

Differentiating features: (1) size (larger and smaller forms), (2) orientation (to the left or right), (3) brightness (middle and outside elements), (4) spatiality (flat figures and illusion of space) and (5) arrangement (symmetry and alternating arrangement).

Common features: (1) shape (all elements), (2) brightness (elements of equal brightness), (3) size (elements of equal size), (4) superimposition (left and right orientations), (5) superimposition (alternating and symmetrical arrangement) and (6) superimposition (space and flatness).

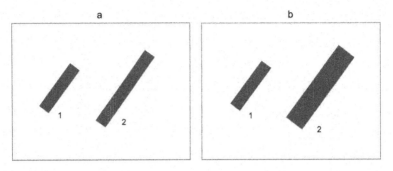

FIGURE 4.3 Strengthening the contrast of two rectangles by increasing the number of their features (common and differentiating).

We have as many as 11 features in total, and the contrast has increased significantly in comparison to Figure 4.2a. This also translates into visual attractiveness.

Figure 4.3a presents two parallel rectangular forms 1 and 2 of different lengths and the same width. Figure 4.3b presents the same forms with the difference of the increasing width of form 2. By increasing the thickness of form 2, we increased the number of features differing forms 1 and 2 by a width feature, but also reduced the number of common features with the same feature. At the same time, however, increasing the width of form 2 caused the proportions of length to width of forms 1 and 2 to become identical, which increased the similarity of their shapes. In this way, with the increased number of distinctive features, the strength/number of common features did not diminish and the contrast increased. Let's count the common and differentiating features of forms 1 and 2 in both illustrations.

Common features:
direction, width.
Differentiating features: length.
There are three features in total.
Common features:
direction, shape (the ratio of width to length is the same).
Differentiating features:
length, thickness.
There are four features in total.

4.2 GOLDEN RATIO

The golden ratio (Latin: *sectio aurea*) is the division of a line in two segments in which the ratio of the longer segment to the shorter segment is the same as the ratio of the entire line to the longer segment. The discovery of the golden ratio is attributed to Pythagoras or his students, and its description to Euclid in the 4th century BC (Heath 1956). Due to its uniqueness, it was and is the subject of fascination and investigation for many centuries (Livio 2003).

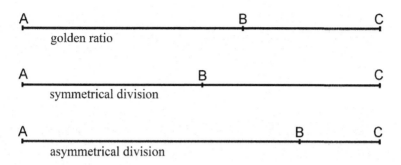

FIGURE 4.4 Three possible divisions of a line into two segments: the golden ratio, symmetrical and asymmetrical.

It is noted that the golden ratio occurs in mathematics (e.g. in geometrical forms and Fibonacci numbers), art, architecture, financial markets and nature.

The psychologist Adolf Zeising, who was mainly interested in mathematics and philosophy, discovered the golden ratio in the arrangement of branches on the trunk of plants and in the nerves of leaves. He extended his research to the skeletons of animals and the branching of their veins and nerves, the proportions of chemical components and the geometry of crystals (Padovan 1999: 305–306).

In 2003, Volkmar and Harald Weiss analyzed psychometric data, concluding that the golden ratio is the basis of the brain wave cycle (Weiss and Weiss 2003). In 2008 this was confirmed experimentally by a team of neuroscientists (Roopun 2008).

The golden ratio also plays an important role in the micro-world. Two scientists J.C.A. Boeyens and D.C. Levendis, in their work *Number Theory and the Periodicity of Matter*, found that stable nucleides obey the principle of golden ratio.

> The most stable arrangement of atomic nuclei is predicted to occur as the ratio of protons to neutrons approaches the golden ratio, $Z/N \rightarrow \tau = 06180$.
>
> **(Boeyens and Levendis 2008)**

How to explain this presence of the golden ratio not only in realms directly related to man but also in nature? Perhaps our analysis will partly clarify this issue. Let us try and accomplish this by using the notion of contrast.

In view of the quantitative nature of its properties, the golden ratio provides a good example for our analysis. Let us see if, in line with our expectations, the line segments reflecting the golden ratio produce the largest contrast; that is, they have the largest number of features. There are three ways to divide a line: the golden ratio, symmetrical division and asymmetrical division. Let's calculate the features that are present here (Figure 4.4).

GOLDEN DIVISION

Differentiating features:

(1) length of segment AB, (2) length of segment BC and (3) length of segment AC.

Common features:

(1) the ratio of AB length to BC length is equal to the ratio of AC to AB.

In this case we have four features in total.

(We've skipped here the common feature resulting from the equality of AB + BC = AC, because this feature has all divisions.)

SYMMETRICAL DIVISION

Differentiating features:

(1) length of segments AB and BC and (2) length of segment AC.

Common features:

(1) length of segment AB is equal to that of segment BC.

In this case we have three features in total.

ASYMMETRICAL DIVISION

Differentiating features:

(1) length of segment AB, (2) length of segment BC and (3) length of segment AC.

Common features:

no common features.

In this case, we have threeatures in total.

As expected, of all possible methods of line division, the golden ratio has the greatest number of features, which indicates that it represents the greatest contrast. Features can be considered as information. More information contained in the same number of elements (which are two segments here) indicates the economy of the means used. This is probably the cause giving rise to more specific features, such as unique properties, visual attractiveness and its presence in nature.

4.3   BINARY MODEL OF VISUAL INTERACTIONS

The previous examples, such as that of the golden ratio, were largely abstract in nature, thus simplifying their analysis. The present example is the most abstract of all (binary), and we will treat it as the model for visual impacts. This example will also prove useful in defining complexity.

Let's consider three (binary) structures composed of eight basic elements: four white squares and four black squares. In order to examine them as visual structures, we count the contrasts and the number of features present in each of them, as done in previous examples.

In Figure 4.5a we notice the following contrasts:

1. Elements (marked with number 1) create a symmetry (contrast) between two white elements located in the middle and two outside black elements. The common feature is the presence of identical elements on both sides

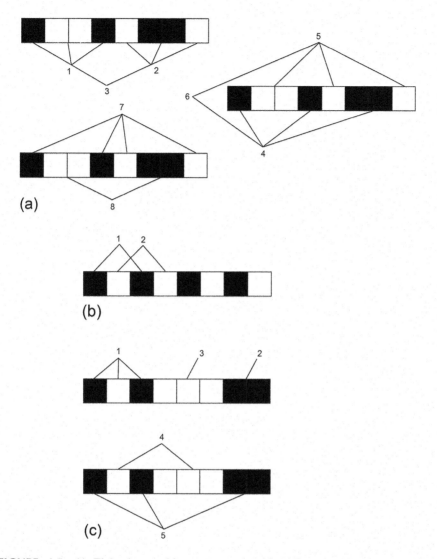

FIGURE 4.5 (a) Eight-element binary structure with eight substructures. (b) Eight-element binary structure with two substructures. (c) Eight-element binary structure with five substructures.

of the symmetric axis, while the differentiating feature is their reverse arrangement.

2. Elements (marked with number 2) create a symmetry (contrast) between two black elements in the middle and two outside white elements. The common feature is the presence of identical elements on both sides of the symmetric axis, while the differentiating feature is their reverse arrangement.

3. Elements (marked with numbers 1 and 2) create an inverted symmetry (contrast), which is marked with number 3. The common feature

is a symmetrical arrangement of elements, while the differentiating feature is brightness.

4. Black elements (double and single) produce a contrast of size. The common feature is blackness, while the differentiating feature is size.

5. White elements (single and double) produce a contrast of size. The common feature is whiteness, while the differentiating feature is size.

6. Black and white elements (marked with numbers 4 and 5) create a symmetry (contrast). The common feature is the placement of black and white elements, while the differentiating feature is brightness.

7. Single elements (white and black) create a contrast of brightness. The common feature is size (singleness), while the differentiating feature is brightness.

8. Double elements (white and black) create a contrast of brightness. The common feature is size (double), while the differentiating feature is brightness.

There are 8 contrasts and 16 features present (the latter have been identified together with the contrasts). Observe that each contrast creates a distinguishable substructure:

1. Symmetry (1)
2. Symmetry (2)
3. Symmetry (3)
4. Black elements (4)
5. White elements (5)
6. Symmetry of black and white (5 and 4)
7. Single elements (7)
8. Doubled elements (8)

Elements of each of these substructures contain common and differentiating features, which is the condition for any substructure to become distinguishable and, simultaneously, the condition for contrast to emerge. In order to estimate the contrast present in a binary structure, it is therefore sufficient to identify and count its substructures. This is a convenient method, which furthermore helps to define the complexity of a binary structure.

When analyzing contrasts, we have not taken into account the differentiating features resulting from the placement of individual elements, because these are uniform for all elements and are of minor importance. Consequently, we have not considered, for example, substructures composed of "single black elements" or "single white elements" because their elements do not create any contrast (have no differentiating features).

In Figure 4.5b, we see the inverted arrangement of white and black elements. Contrasts:

1. Here a contrast is created by white and black elements. The common features are size and quantity of elements, while the differentiating feature is brightness.

Thus, we have here one contrast. Let's see how many substructures can be distinguished. Two substructures stand out: "white elements" and "black elements". However, we should reject them because, as we have pointed out, their elements contain no differentiating features. However, these two substructures connect and produce a contrast to create a structure:

1. Single elements (white and black).

These elements can be considered as a "substructure" superimposed on the entire structure under analysis. Therefore, we have one substructure and a single contrast, which also confirms the observation that the number of contrasts equals that of distinguishable substructures.

In Figure 4.5c we can isolate the following substructures:

1. Single elements (1)
2. White elements (4)
3. Black elements (5)

Other distinguishable elements are a double element (2) and a triple element (3). However, they will not be taken into account here since they are not substructures and do not create contrasts as single elements.

The following contrasts correspond to the identified substructures:

1. Single elements (white and black) create a contrast. The common feature is size, while the differentiating features are brightness and quantity.
2. White elements (a triple white element and a single white element) create a contrast. The common feature is brightness, while the differentiating feature is size.
3. Black elements (a double black element and single black elements) create a contrast of size. The common feature is brightness, while the differentiating features are size and quantity.

For the same number and type of elements (4 white and 4 black), the greatest number of contrasts is offered by the structure shown in Figure 4.5a. That structure is also the most complex (which is consistent with the intuitive criterion) and the most attractive visually.

We can also see—and this is very important—that the abstract binary structure may be analyzed in the same way as visual structures. Thus, it may be stated that the present example establishes the connection between visual impacts and the area of abstract (most general) "impacts". Consequently, the latter can be taken as the model for impacts of any kind (provided that "impacts" are understood as the connection of structures of any type and the contrasts between those structures). Next, we will use this model to define complexity.

REFERENCES

Boeyens, J.C.A. & Levendis, D.C. 2008. *Theory and the Periodicity of Matter.* Netherlands: Springer.

Heath, T.L. 1956. *The Thirteen Books of Euclid's Elements.* New York: Dover Publications.

Livio, M. 2003. *The Golden Ratio: The Story of Phi, The World's Most Astonishing Number.* New York: Broadway Books.

Padovan, R. 1999. *Proportion.* London: Taylor & Francis, 305–306.

Roopun, A.K. 2008. Temporal interactions between cortical rhythms. *Frontiers in Neuroscience* 2(2): 145–154, doi:10.3389/neuro.01.034.2008.

Weiss, V. & Weiss, H. 2003. The golden mean as clock cycle of brain waves. *Chaos, Solitons and Fractals* 18(4): s.643–652, 2003. doi:10.1016/S0960-0779(03)00026-2.

5 Contrast as Complexity

5.1 EQUATING CONTRAST WITH COMPLEXITY

The difficulty of defining complexity is well characterized by Francis Heylighen:

> Complexity has turned out to be very difficult to define. The dozens of definitions that have been offered all fall short in one respect or another, classifying something as complex which we intuitively would see as simple, or denying an obviously complex phenomenon the label of complexity. Moreover, these definitions are either only applicable to a very restricted domain, such as computer algorithms or genomes, or so vague as to be almost meaningless. Edmonds (1996) gives a good review of the different definitions and their shortcomings, concluding that complexity necessarily depends on the language that is used to model the system. Still, I believe there is a common, "objective" core in the different concepts of complexity.
>
> **(Heylighen 1999: 3)**

This chapter and the next one will be devoted to the attempt to formulate such a general definition of complexity which the above text refers to. In accordance with the proposed definition, *when we consider the contrast between two or more visual objects/structures, it grows in intensity as the number/strength of differentiating and common features of contrasting structures/objects increases.*

Such an understanding of contrast remains an intuitive criterion of complexity that can be formulated as follows:

> Let us go back to the original Latin word complexus, which signifies "entwined", "twisted together". This may be interpreted in the following way: in order to have a complex you need two or more components, which are joined in such a way that it is difficult to separate them. Similarly, the Oxford Dictionary defines something as "complex" if it is "made of (usually several) closely connected parts". Here one finds the basic duality between parts which are at the same time distinct and connected. *Intuitively then, a system would be more complex if more parts could be distinguished, and if more connections between them existed.*
>
> **(Heylighen 1999: 3)**

We accept the last sentence as an intuitive criterion: *intuitively then, a system would be more complex if more parts could be distinguished, and if more connections between them existed.* If in this conception of contrast we substitute *differentiating features for distinguishable elements and common features for connections,* we will be able to conclude that contrast is the perception and measure of complexity.

This is quite a surprising but significant association that appeared during the analysis of contrasts in the visual structures. We will now analyze them more in detail.

Note: two types of contrasts can be distinguished: the sensual (physical) contrast, which is determined only by the force of features of contrasting objects, and the mental (abstract) contrast, which depends primarily on the number of these features. (This distinction will be discussed below in the section "Contrast as Compression of Information".) In our considerations, we will deal only with mental contrast.

5.2   ABSTRACT COMPLEXITY DEFINITION

A definition of complexity will be formulated based on an analysis of contrast in the abstract binary structure we have performed in Section 4.3, assuming that determining a complexity for the most general structure will also have a general, model character. We have already established that contrast is a measure of complexity, which is consistent with the aforementioned intuitive criterion: *as a system becomes more complex, the greater is the number of distinguishable elements and the greater the number of connections among them.* Therefore, in order to determine the complexity of a binary structure, we would need to estimate its contrast, that is, count its distinguishable elements (substructures). In Section 4.3, we examined three binary structures, each with the same number of eight basic elements.

Each of them has a different number of substructures and a contrast/complexity that is proportional to the number of substructures.

Another issue that should be investigated is how complexity is affected by the number of basic elements. Let us consider whether structures with the same number of substructures, but with different number of basic elements, would have the same complexity. Intuition tells us that structures that have fewer basic elements, while containing the same or even greater number of substructures, which is indicative of better organisation, are more complex. We may also say that such structures have a higher degree of complexity. The degree of complexity is otherwise the compactness of the form or the compression of information. To express it quantitatively, the degree of complexity would be directly proportional to the number of features and inversely proportional to the number of basic elements (zeros and ones) of a given structure.

$$D = \frac{N}{n}$$

D—degree of complexity
N—number of substructures in a structure
n—number of basic elements (sum of zeros and ones)

The degree of complexity informs us about the internal arrangement of the structure, without providing full information about its complexity, because it does not take into account the size of the structure. For example, the same degree of complexity may be found in structures where the number of basic elements is n = 10 or n = 10,000. Obviously, a structure that has the same degree of complexity but more basic elements must have more distinguishable elements/substructures, which, in turn, according to the intuitive criterion, proves its greater complexity. The definition of complexity should therefore take into account both the degree of complexity (D) and the number of substructures of a given structure (N). We take these variables into account by multiplying them by each other. Thus, the formula for complexity "C" will be as follows:

$$C = D \cdot N = \frac{N}{n} N = \frac{N^2}{n}$$

Complexity defined in this way may be applied not only to binary and visual structures (from which it is derived), but also to all structures that can be recorded in binary format, which (theoretically) means all structures of reality (the first to note the possibility of binary simulation/recording of all physical processes/objects of any complexity was Bertalanffy (1968)).

This definition also meets the intuitive criterion (which has been specified above). Let's analyze it in more detail:

More parts to be represented means more extensive models, which require more time to be searched or computed. Since the components of a complex cannot be separated without destroying it, the method of analysis or decomposition into independent modules cannot be used to develop or simplify such models. This implies that complex entities will be difficult to model, that eventual models will be difficult to use for prediction or control, and that problems will be difficult to solve. This accounts for the connotation of difficult, which the word "complex" has received in later periods.

The aspects of distinction and connection determine two dimensions characterizing complexity. Distinction corresponds to variety, to heterogeneity, to the fact that different parts of the complex behave differently. Connection corresponds to constraint to redundancy, to the fact that different parts are not independent, but that the knowledge of one part allows the determination of features of the other parts. Distinction leads in the limit to disorder, chaos or entropy, like in a gas, where the position of any gas molecule is completely independent of the position of the other molecules. Connection leads to order or negentropy, like in a perfect crystal, where the position of a molecule is completely determined by the positions of the neighbouring molecules to which it is bound. Complexity can only exist if both aspects are present: neither perfect disorder (which can be described statistically through the law of large numbers), nor perfect order (which can be described by traditional deterministic methods) are complex. It thus can be said that complexity is situated between order and disorder, or, using a recently fashionable expression, "on the edge of chaos".

(Heylighen 1999: 3)

The last sentence is misleading because, intuitively, complexity is associated with order but of a higher level, i.e. which organizes more elements. What is suggested above is that the parts/substructures distinction is in opposition to their connections or even excludes each other. It is not possible that particles are both independent and bound at the same time. Only an intermediate state (partial crystallization—edge of chaos) is possible, where some particles become bound at the expense of their independence.

Our considerations deny such reasoning. In the analyses of binary structure (Section 4.5), distinguished parts/substructures such as white elements, double elements, symmetry of elements etc., comprise also, what we can call, connections between them. Connection of elements is not in opposition to their distinction, but makes the distinction even stronger. Consider two elements which have common and different features; e.g. substructure of double elements connect different elements which have the common feature "double-ness". The common features attract those elements making the different features of the contrasting elements stronger. Without connection, different features wouldn't even be noticed (what is the condition of contrast). In the example of structure (Figure 4.5a), substructure "double elements" connects substructure "white elements" and substructure "black elements" (directly double white and double black, and indirectly single white and single black); "symmetrical elements marked 1" connects substructures "single black", "single white" and "double white", indirectly also substructure "double black". It is also easy to see how components are "entwined" here and how difficult it is to separate them without destroying the structure. One can also see duality between parts which are at the same time distinct and connected. Such duality is possible because each element belongs to more than one substructure having more than one feature. Thanks to this, other features are responsible for connections and others for separating (differentiating) elements, and this is the property of all complex objects. The conviction that complexity is situated "on the edge of chaos" is due to the fact that we consider only one feature, in this case, the freedom of the particle, i.e. the gradation of this feature from full freedom (gas) to full restriction of freedom (crystal). One state eliminates here the other. This is a common mistake in the analysis of contrast and complexity, since considering only one feature, we assume in advance that the object is not complex. Let us look at another example, which shows that more features need to be considered:

> Consider the contrast of a light background and a dark figure. If we increase the impact of common features, e.g. by brightening the figure or darkening the background, the contrast decreases. However, if contrasting objects have more features such as a large, bright square and a small dark circle, then strengthening the common features e.g. by darkening the square will increase their contrast (of size and shape) because these features will be compared stronger.

Complex objects have (by definition) more features, which is why some features may be responsible for joining elements (common features) and others for their separation (differing features). If we want to increase the complexity/contrast of an object such as gas, it is important to choose the features that should be strengthened or weakened in order to achieve the desired effect. What features do we have for gas? The distinguishing features are the distinguishing atoms and their states (direction of motion, speed, and location), common features: presence in the considered volume, similarity of atoms (the same gas). The most important distinguishing feature is the separation of individual atoms (without this feature others would not exist). We know that we can increase the contrast by strengthening the common features if we do not significantly weaken the differences and vice versa. In this case, strengthening the common features (ordering of atoms in crystals) will not cause that the atoms will cease to be separated or will be less visible. In the case of crystal formation, common features will be strengthened, at the expense of less significant differentiating characteristics (related to differences in the states of individual atoms). Total contrast and complexity will increase. Therefore, the crystal should be regarded as a more complex object than gas, or state, "on the edge of chaos" (because the common features are weaker here too). Crystallization is also considered an example of emergence, or the emergence of complex wholes from the interaction of simpler components. Generally, this process is characterized by the known rule that *the whole is more than the sum of its parts* (the concept of emergence will be discussed in Chapter 12, "Contrast as Emergence").

5.3   EXISTING DEFINITIONS OF COMPLEXITY

Computational complexity: in computer science, the computational complexity, or simply complexity of an algorithm, is the amount of resources required for running it. The complexity is equal to the number of elementary logical operations that must be performed in the course of the computation. When the nature of the resources is not explicitly given, this is usually the time needed for running the algorithm, and one talks of time complexity. However, this depends on the computer that is used, and time is generally expressed as the number of needed elementary operations. Another resource considered is often the size of the memory that is needed, and then we talk of space complexity. Computational complexity is not a measure of complexity so much as a measure of effort or of the resources required to perform a given task. There are plenty of computations that take a long time and use up lots of space but do not produce anything very complex. So this definition does not meet the intuitive criterion mentioned above.

Algorithmic complexity: algorithmic complexity or algorithmic information content (AIC) was defined by Andrei Nikolaevich Kolmogorov (Kolmogorov 1963) and independently by Ray Solomonoff, and Gregory Chaitin at the beginning of the 1960s. The algorithmic information content of a text or a bit string is equal to the length, in bits, of the shortest computer program that produces that text or bit string as output. This definition, however, like the previous one, does not refer directly to the object itself, but characterizes its complexity through a description. Highly regular, periodic or monotonic strings may be computed by programs that are short and thus contain little information, while random strings require a program that is as long as the string itself, thus resulting in high (maximal) information content. This is clearly counterintuitive, as shown by the example of a monkey typing a text that is more complex than J. Joyce's *Ulysses*. Algorithmic complexity captures the amount of randomness of symbol strings, but is inadequate for applications to coherent structures such as biological or neural systems. It also contradicts computational definition, since short programs computed for a long time have a high computational complexity and small AIC, while random strings with maximal AIC have relatively small computational complexity. However, this definition is widely used in many fields where these applications are not adequate, e.g. in visual perception studies

(Frith and Nias 1974). It probably happens because the definition is most popular and well grounded in science (links to thermodynamics and information theory). Another example is the concept called *Low-Complexity Art*, by a well-known computer scientist—Jürgen Schmidhuber (1997), where he concludes (incorrectly) that the aesthetic attractiveness of objects is inversely proportional to their complexity.

Logical depth (Bennett 1988): it combines two previous complexity definitions: algorithmic complexity and computational complexity (defined as the minimal amount of computational resources (time, memory) needed to solve a given class of problem). Complexity as logical depth refers mainly to the running time of the shortest program capable of generating a given string or pattern. Similar to AIC, complexity as logical depth is a measure of a generative process and does not apply directly to an actually existing physical system or dynamical process. Computing logical depth requires knowing the shortest computer program (which is uncomputable), and thus the measure is subject to the same fundamental limitation as AIC. Let's see how this definition is described by Seth Lloyd, a close associate of Bennett:

> In the early 1980s, Charles Bennett proposed a simple definition of complexity that relies on the trade-off between information and effort. Following Solomonoff, Bennett identified the most plausible explanation of a bit string or data set with the shortest program that produced it. (If there were several programs that were almost as short as the shortest, Bennett included those as plausible explanations, too.) Then Bennett looked at the computational complexity of those short programs. He called this quantity—the effort required to produce the bit string from its most plausible explanation—"logical depth". Of all the measures of complexity Heinz and I studied, logical depth was the most appealing. Bit strings that are obviously simple, like the string consisting of a billion 1's, have short fast-running programs that can produce them (e.g., "PRINT 1 ONE BILLION TIMES") and are logically shallow. Random bit strings (e.g., 11010101100010 … 011, a bit string I got by flipping a coin and calling heads 1 and tails 0) are plausibly produced by long fast-running programs (e.g., "PRINT 11010101100010 … 011") and are also logically shallow. By contrast, bit strings corresponding to the first million digits of π take a long time to produce from their shortest known programs and are logically deep. Logically deep bit strings possess large amounts of structure—structure that takes a long time to compute from the shortest possible program.
>
> **(Lloyd 2006)**

The above description shows that the logical depth to some extent eliminates the disadvantages of computational complexity and AIC, but it is not clear how the labour consumption of generating a given system is correlated with its complexity. It is also not obvious that the longer pi number must be more complex than the shorter one, because the shorter calculation requires less time. An example of the fact that greater labour consumption and a longer system generation time are not associated with increased complexity can be binary numbers, generated in sequence by a short program. If we consider consecutive numbers with the same number of digits (zeros and ones), we will notice that the initial and final numbers have a small complexity, while the numbers in the middle part of the sequence are more complex. Let's see it on the example of numbers in which the number of digits is 5; consecutive numbers are: 10000, 10001, 10010, 10011, 10100, 10101, 10110, 10111, 11000, 11001, 11010, 11011, 11100, 11101, 11110 and 11111. We see that the number 11111 is not the most complex although its calculation takes most of the time.

Despite these inaccuracies, logical depth is quoted (e.g. in cognitive science, biology) as a confirmation of the concept that the increase in the complexity and evolution of biological systems depends on time. Although it seems obvious (even without the application of the definition) that evolution and complexity is growing over time, there is no evidence that this will be the case in the future. In addition, there is also cyclicality in nature, which is associated not only with the increase but also the disappearance of complexity (similar to the binary number). Interestingly, this definition is considered to be the key factor in cognitive science, while, for example, the solution to the mystery of the golden division and the causes for aesthetic preferences are not considered significant (as I had the opportunity to learn in contacts with cognitive scientists), probably because they are not associated with complexity.

Another example, in which the logical depth functions as a confirmation of the complexity of the system, is the fractal patterns that make up, e.g., snowflakes, shoreline or cellular automata. A special supporter of such confirmation is Stephen Wolfram, who was fascinated by the beauty and "complexity" of these patterns, as expressed in his book *New Kind of Science* (Wolfram 2002). He also believes that simple computing systems (such as cellular automata) are better than traditional mathematics to understand the complexity of nature. The complexity of fractal patterns, as well as their aesthetic value, is not confirmed. Judging by the absence of such patterns in art, their aesthetic value (and therefore complexity) is not among the highest.

Effective complexity: this definition of complexity was originally proposed by Murray Gell-Mann (Gell-Mann 1994) and measures the minimal description length of a system's regularities. As such, this measure is related to AIC, but it attempts to distinguish regular features from random or incidental ones and therefore captures how much structure a system contains. The separation of regular features from random ones may be difficult for any given empirical system, and it may crucially depend on criteria supplied by an external observer.

This definition is also not a precise one and fails to take into account the degree of complexity. A structure composed of 10 basic elements has the same complexity as a structure with 10,000 elements, if the description of the regularities is of equal length. This is contrary to what intuition would suggest—namely messages (pictures, texts, formulas) with more content, meanings and regularities are more complex, valuable or preferred, for an equal or smaller number of elements/components, such as, e.g., words.

All the above definitions (except for effective complexity) define the complexity that is not the internal property of the system, but the conditions in which the complexity could arise. Therefore, they also fail to meet the intuitive criterion of complexity which says that *this arrangement is more complex, which contains more distinctive elements and more connections between these elements*. The closest to intuition among the above-mentioned definitions is the effective complexity, which, however, as we have noticed, is not precise. In addition to the aforementioned degree of complexity (which we defined as D = N/n, in our definition), it also does not define what are the regularities to be covered by the shortest description. The Abstract Complexity Definition (ACD) defines regularities as all distinct substructures in a binary structure. The shortest description of regularity (sum of descriptions of individual regularities) in effective complexity corresponds to the number of substructures in ACD (any substructure, even if repeated, is counted here only once, i.e. the number 1 is assigned to it). If there are complex substructures (which include other substructures), also for each such complex substructure, the number 1 is assigned (because their complexity has already been included in the number of substructures). In this way, thanks to the unification consisting in assigning to each substructure the number 1 (instead of its shortest description), we get a very simple formula for complexity, convenient for calculating the complexity of all binary structures. This results directly in the possibility of determining the amount of information, because each extracted substructure is also information (each extraction is also information to which other information can be assigned); in order to know the amount of information, it is enough to count the substructures. However, if we applied the sum of their descriptions here instead of the number of substructures, then the descriptions of complex structures would be duplicated with descriptions of the constituent structures, which would change the value of the calculated complexity and significantly complicate the calculations. Thanks to its simplicity, ACD is also suitable for calculating the complexity of very long binary structures (bit strings), using appropriate algorithms. ACD can be used in all systems in which elements can be distinguished and their features defined (e.g. the golden division has three elements and four features). Because it is defined for a binary structure, which, as the most abstract one, can model all structures of reality (in this consideration, the binary structure was used to model visual interactions), it can be treated as a general complexity model explaining the essence of complexity. ACD also meets and further clarifies the intuitive criterion of complexity formulated above.

Examples: to be specific, let's compare the definitions discussed here in the examples. Table 5.1 summarizes the approximate complexity values of the structures: 10010110 (Figure 4.5a), 10101010 (Figure 4.5b) and 10100011 (Figure 4.5c), for the five definitions of complexity: algorithmic, time, logical depth, effective and abstract, in numbers. These numbers indicate—in the case of *algorithmic complexity*—the number of characters describing a given structure (in intuitive language); in the case of *time and logical depth complexity*—the amount of operations/time needed to generate the structure; and in the case of *effective complexity*, the shortest description of all regularities/substructures of a given structure (as the shortest description, we take here the number of shortest descriptions, assuming that all descriptions have a similar length). As previously noted, the description of complex substructures requires reconsideration of component structures (without which the description would be impossible), and therefore the complexity values are greater here than in the abstract (ACD) definition, which only takes into account the number of all substructures. In the case of abstract complexity, the numbers in the

TABLE 5.1
The Approximate Complexity Values of Three Different Structures, for the Five Definitions of Complexity: Algorithmic, Time, Logical Depth, Effective and Abstract, in Numbers

definition/structure	10010110	10101010	10100011
time complexity	8	8	8
algorithmic complexity	8	2	8
logical depth	8	8	8
effective complexity	22	2	6
abstract complexity	8	1/8	9/8

table mean the number of substructures of a given structure, squared and divided by the number of elements (according to the above formula for complexity). Because in each case, the numbers mean something else; they can't be compared. However, it is possible to compare the complexity values of individual structures for each type of complexity. This comparison shows that the closest intuition is abstract complexity (ACD).

Another example is the application of these three definitions to compare the complexity of the three possible divisions of a segment: golden, symmetric and asymmetric. Algorithmic, time complexity and logical depth are the same for all divisions (the shortest description and the number of operations are identical here), which contradicts intuition and does not explain the aesthetic attractiveness of *golden division*. The abstract complexity is greater for *golden division*, since it has the most attributes (i.e. four), while symmetric and asymmetrical have only three features each, as we have previously calculated. As for the effective complexity, it would also be greater for *golden division* if we considered the proportion of the segments to be a regularity. If we considered only three different lengths of segments, then due to the lack of regularity, the effective complexity would take the value of zero for all divisions.

REFERENCES

Bennett, C.H. 1988. *Logical Depth and Physical Complexity*. In Herken, Rolf (ed.), *The Universal Turing Machine: A Half-Century Survey*. (Oxford University Press, Oxford): 227–257.

Bertalanffy, L. 1968. *General Systems Theory*. New York: G. Brazilier.

Edmonds, B. 1999. What Is Complexity? - The Philosophy of Complexity per se with Application to Some Examples in Evolution. In F. Heylighen & D. Aerts (Eds.) *The Evolution of Complexity*. (Kluwer, Dordrecht).

Frith, C.D. & Nias, D.K.B. 1974. What determines aesthetic preferences? *Journal of General Psychology* 91: 163–173.

Gell-Mann, M. 1994. *The Quark and the Jaguar*. Canada: H. Fenn & Company Ltd.

Heylighen F. 1999. The Growth of Structural and Functional Complexity during Evolution, in; F. Heylighen, J. Bollen & A. Riegler (Eds.) *The Evolution of Complexity*. (Kluwer Academic, Dordrecht): 17–44.

Kolmogorov, A. 1963. On Tables of Random Numbers. *Sankhya A*. 25: 369–375.

Lloyd, S. 2006. *Programming the Universe*. New York: Alfred A. Knopf.

Schmidhuber, J. 1997. Low Complexity Art. *Leonardo. MIT Press* 30(2): 97–103.

Wolfram, S. 2002. *A New Kind of Science*. Wolfram Media INC.

6 Contrast as Compression of Information

6.1 INFORMATION COMPRESSION AS A CAUSE OF AESTHETIC PREFERENCES

Data compression (in information theory) consists of changing the way information is stored so as to reduce redundancy and thus the volume of the set. In other words, it is about expressing the same set of information but using fewer bits. Fewer bits are also less energy. As we know from information theory, reception, transmission and storage of data require some energy (it is estimated that for 1 bit of information, about 0.7 kT is required, where k = Boltzmann constant and T = temperature in Kelvin scale (Brillouin 2004)). By reducing the number of bits, compression of information decreases the amount of energy required. To illustrate, this is why taking advantage of the compression function in a digital camera greatly increases the number of pictures we can take, with higher resolution and the same usage of the battery (Sadler and Martonosi 2006). Objects/structures of greater complexity include those that contain the same or greater number of features (features can be identified with information) in a more succinct form, colloquially speaking. The succinct format directly brings to mind the compression of information. Examples of more complex/compressed objects are a shorter text with the same or more content, a concise announcement, coherent scientific theory (e.g. $E = mc^2$), ambiguous artwork, a melodic musical composition as well as spatial objects and their illusions (e.g. in painting). Such objects/structures are in general more preferred, even though it is hardly intuitive that such preferences are mostly due to the complexity/compression of information. Let's try to explain why. First of all, perceiving more compressed objects saves energy (because our mind receives the same amount of information contained in fewer bits). Consequently, perception becomes easier, more economic and pleasurable, which can be compared to, for example, quicker and easier learning or acquisition of knowledge, which also contributes to our development. The development is generally what we prefer, and even more the development, that requires less effort. Hence the result of our aesthetic preferences and beauty experience.

Note: in our definition of complexity, we have identified the compression of information with the degree of complexity (D = N/n), which determines the degree of organization and conciseness of the structure/object. However, we defined complexity as the product of the degree of complexity, i.e. information compression (D) and the number of object features (N) which determines the size of the compressed structure ($C = D \times N = N^2/n$). We see here that the essence of complexity and information compression is the same; the difference is only due to the size of the structure.

6.2   PERCEPTUAL ANALYSIS OF CONTRAST

According to the definition of contrast, contrast grows stronger as there are more numerous/stronger common and differentiating features held by contrasting objects. Let us define more precisely what "more numerous/stronger" (features) means. Contrast affects both our senses and the mind, and each type of impact is different in nature. The mental contrast is a measure of complexity, and its magnitude depends on the number of features (items of information) found in contrasting objects. Its impact consists of the experience of pleasure derived from the ease (cost-effectiveness) with which new information is assimilated and the emergence of new opportunities for our mind (new structural linkages facilitating development/growth of the mind) due to the surfeit of features being connected without any additional expenditure of energy. The material (sensory) contrast depends only on the energy contained in individual features and can be identified with physical force. Impacts of both types of contrast may be either relatively independent (e.g. reading a book or hearing a rifle shot) or occur simultaneously, as when (complex) text is being read aloud, when a large painting is contemplated and when one listens to loud music. Typically, both types of contrast include features of varied energy. When impacts (energy) of particular features of perceived objects differ, then external stimuli carrying information (features) that reach the brain by way of the senses have varied energy, too. In contrast, the stimuli within the brain are equipped with the same amount of energy. Energy-based differentiation occurs through changes in impulse frequencies (Pouille and Scanziani 2004). Such dissimilar frequencies can be considered additional features (in fact, these are features of features), which add to the number of features found in a specific structure/object in our mind. In this sense, the strength of impacts produced by the features influences complexity and mental contrast. However, when energy is increased proportionally for all the features, this only makes their impacts stronger and has no effect on complexity or mental contrast. Physical impacts are also covered by the general definition of contrast as tensions between impacts of the common and the differentiating features of the objects under analysis. Some examples:

1. The interaction between two objects (particles) with different momenta that encounter each other (collide) in a given space also involves the impacts of their common features (location in space) and the features that differentiate them (different momenta).
2. A rubber band extended by hands (tightly stretched) has some common features (connections with hands) and also differentiating features (the direction of the force of the elastic and that of the hands is opposite), thus giving rise to tension.
3. The word "tension" could be associated with the difference of electric potentials, e.g. a battery which starts operating (current flow as impact) when a connection (common feature) is made between different potentials (different features).

The existing knowledge does not explain what the impact (interaction in general) is and fails to associate it with the contrast or tension between features held in common (which link objects) or the differentiating features (which distinguish objects, set them apart). For example, Wikipedia offers the following definitions of the term "interaction":

a. Interaction (impact) is a kind of action that occurs as two or more objects have an effect upon one another. The term "interaction (impact)" is used in various sciences for different purposes.
b. In physics and chemistry, it refers to the force exerted by one object on another, and it is measured by the energy of such interaction (impact).

Both of these definitions fail to explain what interaction is in its essence.

6.3 DISTINCTION BETWEEN ART AND BEAUTY

So far, analyzing mental contrast, we have taken into account the number and strength of contrasting objects features, but we did not take into account their meaning which can be both positive and negative. Consider the following mental contrast: we get some negative information that moves us, and we experience unpleasant feelings. The negativity of information is in contradiction with the pleasure of high contrast/complexity perception (resulting from the perception economy). Would that contradict our previous considerations? Let's try to explain it. Negative information is information about something opposite to contrast, development, complexity, integration or information about destruction. The information itself, however, is not destructive because it enriches our mind and develops it. The resulting pleasure overlaps with the unpleasantness associated with the feeling of destruction. These two feelings, however, do not cancel each other because they have different characters/qualities. The feeling of pleasure is of an abstract nature connected with development in general, whereas the negative feeling is associated with a specific context. These two feelings interact in a different way and also create a contrast with each other. This additional contrast enhances the total contrast contained in the message under consideration. Negative meanings appeared in a radical way in art at the beginning of the 20th century.

> During the 20th century both theorists and artists concluded that beauty is a defective concept and it is not possible to construct its theory. Neither is this property so valuable as believed for centuries. The ability of an artwork to shock the observer is more important than that it delights with its beauty. This shock is achieved not only by beauty, but even through ugliness. Nowadays we like ugliness as much as beauty, wrote Apollinaire.
>
> **(Tatarkiewicz 1980)**

In this way, art, introducing negative meanings, significantly widened the range of contrasts (means of expression) in relation to the earlier period, associated with beauty. So art is a broader concept than beauty.

REFERENCES

Brillouin, L. 2004. *Science and Information Theory*. Dover: Mineola.
Pouille, F. & Scanziani, M. 2004. Routing of spike series by dynamic circuits in the hippocampus. *Nature* 429: 717–723.
Sadler, C.M. & Martonosi, M. 2006. *Data Compression Algorithms for Energy-Constrained Devices in Delay Tolerant Networks. Proceedings of the 4th International Conference on Embedded Networked Sensor Systems*. New York: ACM, 265–278.
Tatarkiewicz, W. 1980. *A History of Six Ideas: An Essay in Aesthetics*. Boston: Kluwer.

7 Contrast as Development

If we reach to modern sources of knowledge (literature and internet), we will not find in them philosophical considerations analyzing and defining the concept of development in the general sense. As in the case of contrast, beauty, complexity, value etc., development is defined and studied only within specific areas. So we have economic, social, biological, intellectual, emotional, physical development, etc., but we do not know what all these types of development have in common (apart from the name "development"); we do not know what development is in the general sense. Existing encyclopaedic definitions rather explain the functioning of this concept in linguistic contexts than explaining its essence. One such definition can be found here (https://encyklopedia.pwn.pl/haslo/rozwoj;4009883.html):

> Development: (1) any long-lasting process of directional changes, in which the following stages of changes (development phases) of a given object (system) can be distinguished correctly, showing the evident differentiation of this object in a given respect; (2) the process of directional transformations in the course of which objects (systems) of a given kind pass from simple, lower, less perfect forms to more complex, higher, perfect forms or states, in a given respect; the notion of development understood in this way is closely related to the concept of progress, especially in colloquial speech and older scientific literature.

We will continue our considerations based on the definition of contrast and its further analysis and try to understand what development is in general (which is its essence). When observing a contrast, we also observe the connection between contrasting objects/structures (resulting from their common features) and the emergence of a new, more complex structure possessing the common and differentiating features of connected structures. In the general sense, the emergence of a new structure is tantamount to development. Therefore, it may be stated that *contrast is the perception of structure connections, that is, the perception and experience of development* (development of our imagination in this case). A similar understanding of development as a synthesis through contrast, we can also find in Whitehead's cosmology: *Process and Reality* (Whitehead 1978), where contrasts are described as:

> Modes of Synthesis of Entities in one Prehension or patterned Entities. The eighth category includes an indefinite progression of categories as we proceed from "contrasts" to "contrasts of contrasts" and on indefinitely to higher grades of contrasts.

Structures participating in a contrast may be said to include the observer's imagination structure. Contrasts arise both between the structures being currently perceived and between those structures and the structure of the observer's memory, which also contributes to the development of his/her imagination. These relations have been theorized in a similar way by Versace et al. (2009):

> Various forms of knowledge are stored in long-term memory in various formats associated with different sensory modalities. We are able to associate quickly and blend such varying information in our memories as a creative process of remembering that meshes with unfolding present experience.

The joining of structures does not occur instantaneously. Development should be considered here as a process which begins when we first note a contrast that motivates us to acquire information about it (it stimulates our interest due to information compression, which, in line with our previous findings, accelerates and makes more pleasant the acquisition of information).

In the course of our analysis we gain information that increases our knowledge of the perceived structures. This in turn causes the number of common features to increase, while reducing the number of differentiating features (since common features replace differentiating features). The contrast stops being an effective force when there are too few differentiating features to enrich our imagination any more. Our imagination has stopped developing.

In practice, it works this way that when we are affected by something, something attracts our attention, shocks us (e.g. as happens in art), that is when we notice a major contrast; this already indicates that structures are being intensively connected. An example may be the first exhibition of the impressionists (who violated the rules of academic painting), Picasso's *Les Demoiselles d'Avignon* (description found at: www.moma.org/collection/works/79766) or Duchamp's *Fountain* https://en.wiki pedia.org/wiki/Fountain_(Duchamp), where new artworks and our prior notions of them were being juxtaposed. In time, as we familiarize ourselves with these works, they acquire more features in common with our imagination. Differentiating features usually become weaker, such as when we are no longer shocked by the depiction of a deformed face or the exhibition of a ready-made object in an art gallery. In time, the contrast grows smaller, while our imagination develops. When further development is no longer possible, we lose interest (in the sense of having an aesthetic experience) in the artwork.

REFERENCES

Versace, R., Labeyea, E., Badarda, G. & Rosea, M. 2009. The contents of long-term memory and the emergence of knowledge. *European Journal of Cognitive Psychology* 21(4): 522–560.

Whitehead, A.N. 1978. *Process and Reality*. New York: A Division of Macmillan Publishing Co, Inc.

8 Contrast as Value

8.1 VALUE AS DEVELOPMENT

Various theories have been put forward in the West to try and define what a value "is"—as opposed to saying what kinds of value a thing may "have". There are generally held to be three kinds of theory at present that attempt to answer the question of what a value is and these have been borrowed from the field of ethics. Each group of theories tends to concentrate on different aspects of the subject so that if ethics can be defined as, say, the principles governing the conduct of a person then the first group of theories (ontology and deontology) looks at the principles themselves, the second group of theories (teleology and consequentialism) looks at the aims and outcomes of conduct, and the third group of theories (virtue ethics and fitting-attitude theory) looks at the concept of the person, their character and attitudes.

(https://en.wikipedia.org/wiki/Values_(Western_philosophy))

We will not analyze the above theories as well as others and concentrate only on what is missing, that is, on explaining the essence of values and formulating its general definition. There are many different types of values and their classifications. As an example, we will use the list of values proposed by William Frankena in his book *Ethics* (Frankena 1963):

1. Beauty, harmony, proportion, aesthetic experience
2. Moral disposition, virtue, pleasure, happiness, contentment
3. Truth, knowledge, understanding, wisdom, honour, esteem
4. Life, health, strength, peace, security
5. Love, affection, friendship, cooperation
6. Power, achievement, freedom, adventure, novelty

If we consider what is common to these diverse types of values, we note that all of them contribute to some extent to our development (growth). As was proven earlier, development may be equated with contrast and complexity. Consequently, *contrast and complexity can be considered as a measure of value in the general sense and its essence.* The use of this general measure of value in practice may, on the one hand, consist of assessing the value of considered objects (i.e. their contrast, complexity and information compression) and improving the value of objects by increasing their compression (compressing the information contained therein). In this way, we improve, for example, the text by increasing its brevity, choosing more appropriate words, eliminating the unnecessary, etc. Generally, everything that is more valuable (both abstract and specific) also has greater complexity, information compression and contrast. We have shown this in many different examples, including the most general one which is the binary structure; this will also be confirmed by further examples (Chapter 9: "Examples of Contrasts in Artworks").

8.2   CONTRAST AS THE ABSTRACT VALUE—DEFINITION OF ART

As formal elements of contemporary artworks can belong to any sphere of reality (as discussed in Chapter 2), all the aforementioned values can be present in works of art today. They can also perform an aesthetic function (an aesthetic function is understood here broadly also as an artistic function) and therefore have aesthetic value. Of the listed values only aesthetic has such an (overriding, generic) attribute that it can cover all other values. Such an attribute has abstract concepts (e.g. the concept of chair covers all types of chairs). Therefore aesthetic value should be understood as a value in the abstract sense. So we can say that *the essential characteristic of art, what marks it out, is that (unlike all the other aspects of our life) it represents the value in the abstract.* What is meant here is not abstract art as such. We classify as art also realistic, impressionist, conceptual or any other movement of art because they express first and foremost the abstract value. Picasso or Duchamp used ready-made objects (e.g. urinal), not to express their utility value, but to use it to express value in general. If photography presents a social problem, it can be considered as art, not because it shows, e.g. human harm and arouses sympathy, but because it contains value in general (that is, complexity and contrast). Just expressing this value is a function of art. Therefore, we cannot define art (in a simple way), because whatever we point (e.g. that it is a game, it represents cognitive or moral values, it is shocking or it has harmonious shapes), it is not art. This relates to the ever-changing nature of art, which prevents it from being associated, other than fleetingly, with any specific sphere of reality, other than art itself. An attempt to differentiate art is important since it defines art's potential for enriching human life. Then, the higher the abstract value (i.e. the more pronounced contrast and greater complexity) of the artwork, the stronger the distinction. It does not matter, however, what specific spheres of reality are associated with the work of art in question. Since the contrast, complexity and value (understood here as synonyms) in the abstract sense distinguish art (from reality), they also define it. The definition of art can thus be formulated as follows: *art and beauty are identified with strong contrast or high complexity understood as abstract values.*

REFERENCE

Frankena, W.K. 1963. *Ethics*. Eaglewood Cliffs: Prentice-Hall, 87–88.

9 Examples of Contrasts in Artworks

Figure 9.1 depicts one of the earliest human paintings (Lascaux Cave 17000–15000 BC). Unquestionably, the first human paintings imitating reality impressed us in the past and still do today. Our investigations so far suggest that they should comprise a big contrast. It may be assumed that what impresses us the most is the appearance of something that looks like reality but is not reality, which is new but familiar at the same time, which has features in common with reality and us, that is, with our imagination. The shapes that have been abstracted from reality previously existed only in our imagination. In contrast, a drawing has features that come from imagination and from reality. It can be described as a new structure that connects the structure of reality and its image through the feature of shape. Thus, it is also a contrast between image and reality. The combination of these structures can be considered one of the greatest human discoveries. Since then, relationships between imagination and reality have been strengthened in subsequent periods of history (art) by increasing the number of common features. Imagination is also a structural model of reality, created in the mind of a human being. The more common features this model has with reality, the stronger it is perceived (the greater the contrast).

FIGURE 9.1 *Lascaux Cave*: one of the earliest human paintings (17000–15000 BC).
Note: This file (as Lascaux II) is licensed under the Creative Commons Attribution 2.0 Generic license. https://commons.wikimedia.org/wiki/File:Lascaux_II.jpg

The art of Ancient Greece: its duration is assumed to be from about 1200 BC until the 1st century BC. Ancient Greek art stands out among that of other ancient cultures for its development of naturalistic but idealized depictions of the human body, in which, largely, nude male figures were generally the focus of innovation. The Greek painters attained such a considerable skill in recreating reality that they could create its illusion (illusionism). The outstanding representatives included Zeuxis of Heraclea, Parrhasius of Ephesus and Timanthes of Cythnus. The anecdote tells of the birds flying to the Zeuxis-painted grapes and the reaction of the people at the sight of the painted drapery on the wall—the curtains of Parrhasius. Already then, however, both in Greek and Egyptian art, the imitative recreation of reality was deliberately abandoned in favour of abstract structures and orders. The so-called Great Theory of Beauty was set up, from which it resulted that *beauty depends on the selection of proportions and the proper arrangement of parts, and more precisely, on the size, quality and quantity of parts and on their mutual relation* (Tatarkiewicz 1980). The Pythagoreans invented the golden division (discussed above), which they considered the most advantageous, and applied it in painting, sculpture and architecture. This invention was very important for art as the discovery of objective beauty.

The Middle Ages: an epoch in the history of Europe lasting from the 5th century to the 15th century, which began with the fall of the West Roman Empire and lasted until the Renaissance. The entire culture of the Middle Ages is connected with the birth and development of Christianity. Christianity, neither in the Middle Ages nor in later ages, created its own aesthetic doctrine. For a long time in medieval art, there were formal elements of antiquity, in particular realistic imaging, which were applied to abstract notions and immaterial phenomena. The art of the European Middle Ages, up to the end of the international Gothic phase, is the art of symbols directing our thoughts to the world of objectively existing values (therefore it is difficult to understand without knowledge of Christian iconography), and its subject is focused on the relationship between man and God. The combination of religious symbolism with formal elements of antiquity did not create a coherent, integral whole. Conceptual/semantic structures are created according to different rules than visual structures; therefore their relationship could only be superficial (few common features). The overall contrast could not be so strong.

The Renaissance: it was a cultural movement that profoundly affected European intellectual life in the early modern period. Beginning in Italy, and spreading to the rest of Europe by the 16th century, its influence was felt in literature, philosophy, art, music, politics, science, religion and other aspects of intellectual inquiry.

The discovery of a geometrical perspective in painting made the connection of reality with its imagination even more powerful. An important role was played by space as a very strong, common feature of perspective, drawing/image and reality. The contrast that we perceive here arises from combining the structure of reality with the structure of the image and is so large because the common and differing features of these structures are very strong. Because the Renaissance paintings, despite their illusive similarity to reality, were designed and composed, great attention was also paid to the organization of visual structures. A good example here is *The Last Supper* by Leonardo da Vinci (Figure 9.2), so thoroughly studied by painters until today.

FIGURE 9.2   *The Last Supper* (Leonardo da Vinci 1494).
Note: This work is in the public domain in its country of origin and in other countries and areas where the copyright term is the author's life plus 100 years or fewer. This work is in the public domain in the United States because it was published (or registered with the U.S. Copyright Office) before January 1, 1925.

This work has been subject to multiple interpretations, primarily from the point of view of its contents, for example, that it represents Christ's announcement that he would be betrayed and the agitation visible on the faces of the Apostles. However, the author incorporated numerous interesting formal contrasts, which are less apparent to viewers. These contrasts include:

1. Christ's head placed in a central perspective strongly links the figure of Christ to the structure of space (differentiating features). As a result, the area of superimposition of these elements (a common feature) is reinforced, gains additional meaning and makes Christ's figure appear larger.
2. A major contrast is created between the person of Christ and the groups of three Apostles.
   The common features are similar size, colours (blue and red), distance from the closest group and being located along the same line. The differentiating feature is the number of individuals. Owing to this strong connection (by common features) between the person of Christ and the groups of three Apostles, the differentiating features, such as triple-ness, are in a way indirectly attached to the former. Consequently, Christ seems to be a triple human being, which strongly contrasts with the fact that He is only a single person. The trait of triple-ness has also a religious significance, since God is present as three persons: God the Father, God the Son and God the Holy Spirit.
3. The contrast also creates blue and red spots (garments), appearing alternately. Common features: number (four spots), size, distance, occurrence of two colours within the same group; differentiating features: colour. Thanks to the common features, the colour's effect (contrast) is enhanced.

Baroque: it was a movement in the European culture, which dates from the end of the 16th century to the middle of the 18th century. It included all manifestations of literary and artistic activities. It was based on the creative transformation of Renaissance classicism in the pursuit of maximum impact on the viewer. In painting, it looked as follows:

> Baroque painters worked deliberately to set themselves apart from the painters of the Renaissance and the Mannerism period after it. In their palette they used intense and warm colors, and particularly made use of the primary colors red, blue and yellow, frequently putting all three in close proximity. They avoided the even lighting of Renaissance painting and used strong contrasts of light and darkness on certain parts of the picture to direct attention to the central actions or figures. In their composition, they avoided the tranquil scenes of Renaissance paintings, and chose the moments of the greatest movement and drama. Unlike the tranquil faces of Renaissance paintings, the faces in Baroque paintings clearly expressed their emotions. They often used asymmetry, with action occurring away from the center of the picture, and created axes that were neither vertical nor horizontal, but slanting to the left or right, giving a sense of instability and movement. They enhanced this impression of movement by having the costumes of the personages blown by the wind, or moved by their own gestures. The overall impressions were movement, emotion and drama. Another essential element of baroque painting was allegory; every painting told a story and had a message, often encrypted in symbols and allegorical characters, which an educated viewer was expected to know and read.
>
> **(https://en.wikipedia.org/wiki/Baroque)**

The above description defines how individual formal means of the Renaissance were strengthened in Baroque painting, in both visual—colour, space, movement—and meaning—rich symbolism, allegories, historical and religious themes. Baroque, therefore, did not introduce new formal means, but intensified the existing ones. Although it was more than stylization, the introduced changes were not significantly deep and were in the quantitative sphere rather than qualitative. The contrast in relation to the Renaissance consisted in the introduction of differentiating features so as to preserve important common features. The changes took place here inside of the same qualities.

Mannerism: a style in European art, occurring from about 1520 to the end of the 16th century and characterized by striving for formal and technical perfection of the work, as well as refinement, sophistication and freedom of form. It was also important to surprise the viewer and apply unusual solutions, illusion and fantasy. Among the more important features specific to Mannerism painting, one can also mention the lack of realistic imitation of nature, the use of extended proportions of the human body, resignation from a convergent perspective or, on the contrary, its extreme accentuation in supernaturally long sceneries. The works often had an allegorical meaning with the accumulation of complicated symbolism. The readable and bright Renaissance compositional canons were abandoned, and a large accumulation of figures was used, which gave the impression of crowding. Colouring was often unreal. Direct pursuit of surprise, amazement of the viewer, without a deeper and formal analysis, did not give the expected results here. If they appear only in the outer layer, they are superficial and insignificant. The striving to create the impression here was to weaken the essential features common to the previous movements (Renaissance, Baroque), in exchange for the introduction of non-significant differentiating features (stylization). Instead of increasing, the contrast has weakened.

Classicism: the main representative of classicism in painting was a French painter, Jacques-Louis David (1748–1825). He was also an official artist of the French Revolution, he created a clear and bearable revolutionary symbol—*Oath of the Horatii*. The realistically captured *Death of Marat* is also connected with the revolution. These paintings are examples of engaged (politically) art, often criticized by supporters of autonomous (independent) art. They do not bring new formal means to painting, but use already existing ones, for the realization of non-artistic goals. Therefore, the visual contrast here is weak: there are no differentiating features.

Romanticism: it was created as a reaction to social and political changes caused by the industrial revolution and the French Revolution of 1789. It was a form of rebellion against the established social rules that ruled the societies of the Enlightenment era—against the rigid rules of aristocracy and townspeople life and against the scientific approach to nature and man. The Romantic style also did not formally contribute to painting. In relation to the previous period, the changes included: rich colour, contrasting chiaroscuro, soft modelling, emphasizing the textural values of the canvas and dynamizing the composition. However, these were not new features; similar changes were introduced earlier by Baroque in relation to Renaissance.

Realism: it is a direction that strengthens the common features of an artwork with reality through its observation, description and imitation. Because the differences (between artworks and reality) are strong enough (the picture is always different from the real landscape), the contrast increases. Increasing the impact of features in common with nature is also a condition for the occurrence of contrast, in accordance with the principle that the objects which are more similar create contrast first. Therefore, Realism (as long as the differentiating characteristics interact) is always able to affect. However, if the differing features (although they do occur) are repeated too long, they become, to a large extent, features common to our imagination. Then the contrast decreases as a result of the weakening of the differentiating features. They can then be increased by introducing new features to the artwork and moving away from reality, as was done in Impressionism, Cubism and Surrealism. Artists such as Picasso and Cézanne, however, stressed the need to remain in a strong relationship with nature.

Impressionism: it was a trend in European art that was initiated by a group of Paris artists studying at Atelier Gleyère and at Académie Suisse in the second half of the 19th century. Eight Parisian exhibitions in the years 1874–1886 resulted in the breaking of a new art with academism, in force in the second half of the 19th century. It was a turning point and opened the era of modernism. This breakthrough consisted primarily in abstracting colour as one of the most important visual structures. How can one understand the abstraction of colour in an image? Like all great discoveries in painting, Impressionism was created during the careful observation of nature. The effect of light on the local colour of objects was noticed, which was not the same at different times of the day and in different colour combinations. Colour was not as bound up with an object as before, but it more strongly came in interactions with other colours and formal elements, such as shape, size and brightness.

The key discovery was the contrast of complementary colours and its impact on physiology of vision. In short, it can be described as follows: if we look at a colour, for example, red, and then move our eyes to white, it will not seem white, but green. This is because the red light receptors after previous observation of a strong monochrome dose of red are no longer so sensitive to a weaker dose of this colour, contained in white light, and therefore send a weaker signal to the brain than the green light receptors, which did not work before. Impressionists by placing patches of complementary colours next to each other, in this way, facilitated the regeneration of "exhausted" receptors, thus supporting the physiology of vision. It also has a significant impact on the pleasure of looking at impressionist paintings. By explaining this phenomenon with the principle of contrast, we can say that the impact of common features of sight and colour has been increased (by allowing proper vision of colour), as well as the strength of the differentiating features has been increased by combining complementary colours (strongly different). Thanks to this, the contrast increased significantly.

Another aspect of this discovery was the divisionism method (connected with Claude Monet's artistic search) developed by neo-impressionists into the so-called pointillism (whose main representatives were Georges Seurat and Paul Signac). Divisionism consists in limiting the colour palette of the solar spectrum. Paints are applied with patches of "pure" colours, which, observed from a distance, merge in the viewer's retina. In this way, the effect of vibration and luminosity is obtained, which is impossible to achieve when mixing colours. It could be explained as follows:

> If red, blue, and green light (the additive primaries) are mixed, the result is something close to white light (see Prism (optics)). Painting is inherently subtractive, but Pointillist colours often seem brighter than typical mixed subtractive colours. This may be partly because subtractive mixing of the pigments is avoided, and because some of the white canvas may be showing between the applied dots.
>
> **(https://en.wikipedia.org/wiki/Pointillism)**

The discovery of the pointillist method also proved to be pioneering for contemporary printing techniques. Also televisions and computer monitors use a similar technique to represent image colours using red, green and blue (RGB).

Post-Impressionism (i.e. art after Impressionism): this term is used to describe various phenomena in French art at the turn of the 19th and 20th centuries, resulting from Impressionism. Outstanding representatives of this trend include Vincent van Gogh, Paul Gauguin, Paul Cézanne and Henri Toulouse-Lautrec. Post-impressionists continued the colour exploration and at the same time rejected many principles of the original Impressionism. They tried to free an image from the imitation of nature, that is, the concept of mimesis, and emphasized the autonomy of the painting. For many artists, post-Impressionism was the starting point in the pursuit of their own style. While in the Impressionism, colour gained autonomy; in post-Impressionism, it still had a very important function, but already in connection with a compact, defined form. Particularly important and revealing during this period was the painting of Paul Cézanne (considered the father of modernism), where the beginnings of

Cubism and abstract art were already visible. While preserving the impressionist achievements, Cézanne further strengthened the structure of space, which increased the number and strength of contrasts.

In *Still Life with Green Pot and Pewter Jug* (Figure 9.3), it is noteworthy that all elements of the picture are doubled. There are two jugs, two onions, two eggs, two section of the table separated by a tablecloth, two sections of the tablecloth separated by a knife, two distinguishable parts of the knife and also an apple and a small dish that are similar in size and form. If we consider why the painter introduced the trait of double-ness so consistently, we will conclude that this provided all the elements of the painting with an additional common feature (double-ness). As a result, the effect of differentiating features became stronger, thus increasing the contrast. We may also notice a contrast of meanings between *still life* and *double-ness*, for which the common feature is superimposition. This example demonstrates Cézanne's conceptual approach to painting. A large share of knowledge in Cézanne's work is also confirmed by the well-thought-out composition of his paintings, subordinated to either geometric (Figure 11.19) or objective (Figure 9.4) structures. It is also worth paying attention to the deviation from the illusive presentation of reality. Jugs have different tilt angles towards the viewer. The left one is more visible from above and the right

FIGURE 9.3 *Still Life with Green Pot and Pewter Jug* (Cézanne 1870). It should be noted that all elements of this picture are doubled. There are two jugs, two onions, two eggs, two table sections separated by a tablecloth, two sections of the tablecloth separated by a knife, two distinguishable parts of the knife and also an apple and a small dish that are similar in size and form.

FIGURE 9.4 Cézanne, *The Bathers* (208 × 249 cm, 1898–1905). By imposing the face on the elements of the landscape in this painting, they gain additional features. Trees resemble (overlap) hair, spots of leaves—eyes and hands—beard.
Note: This work is in the public domain in its country of origin and in other countries and areas where the copyright term is the author's life plus 100 years or fewer.

one from the side, which is their important difference. This contrast, which Cézanne often used in his paintings and was its inventor, was important because he took into account the influence of memory and knowledge on the imagination and vision. Although this influence has always existed, only deformation allowed its disclosure. This discovery is also the starting point for Cubism.

Another example of enhancing contrast by overlapping structures in the image is Figure 9.4. This time, Cézanne imposed the form and meaning of a face on the landscape. The sloping trees resemble hair, patches of leaves—eyes, and the oval of the face closes the layout of women's hands. Thanks to this imposition, all elements of the picture gain double meaning. The face, however, is not clearly visible (is ambiguous) and is not easily recognizable (as it is recognizable in Figure 9.13 which is more like a joke than a work of art). Thanks to this, the hidden meaning does not dominate and does not weaken other meanings this way, but adds to them, strengthening the contrast.

If we consider the picture as a link between imagination and reality, we can say that taking into account the influence of thinking is an additional common feature here. We get to know reality by observing and remembering, creating imaginary structural models that have a large number of features in common with the structure of reality. Some of these features are simply our knowledge. The stimuli reaching us through the senses are compared with our model, and depending on the number of features/structures shared by the model with the stimulus, the perception is stronger or weaker. If we know an object well, we have many of its structural features in imagination. Recalling any feature of the object, e.g. by observing it, immediately evokes other related characteristics. These other features, because they do not occur in the observation, are much weaker. Cubistic image, depicting the view of objects from different sides, takes into account these features, while at the same time weakening the perceptual features (currently perceived). Considering the fact that realistic representations are well known, despite their deformation, objects are still recognizable and take part in contrast.

9.1 EXAMPLES OF CONTRASTS IN PICASSO PAINTINGS

In the painting *Woman with a Crow* (Figure 9.5), a slight deformation of the woman's arms by lifting them (strengthened by the back of the chair) makes her similar to the bird. As a result of this deformation, the woman's form gains an additional feature— the meaning of the bird. The number of common features of the woman and the bird increases, which increases the contrast. When we deal with objects in an image, their

FIGURE 9.5 Picasso, *Woman with a Crow* (charcoal, pastel and watercolour on paper, 64.6 × 49.5 cm, 1904). © Succession Picasso 2021.

meanings also have impact on the contrast. Meanings, like forms, are structures but with a large number of non-visual features. These features are not directly perceived by the senses as the features of visual forms, hence the difference in their perception. However, we can compare and sum them together.

Figure 9.6 shows Picasso's painting entitled *Woman with Joined Hands* (1907). This is an example of a shared participation of visual and semantic features in the contrast. There are contrasts of forms and meanings of particular objects (eyes, lips, hair, shadow etc.). Picasso, for increasing the contrast, changes (deforms) the forms of objects similar in meaning, that is, strongly connected, for example, through symmetry (such as, symmetrical parts of the face or eyes). If the left and right eye in our image have the same forms and meanings, the contrast between them is weak (no differences). By changing the brightness of one eye, Picasso introduces a differentiating feature, slightly weakening the coherence of the strongly bound (identical) eye structure. The lack of contrast/interaction in the case of identical eyes is replaced here by the effect that the eyes now have the same meanings (common feature) and other forms (different feature). One can also do the opposite: give the same form (e.g. brightness and shape) to other objects (right eye and mouth), then the common feature is the form and the difference is the

FIGURE 9.6   Picasso, *Woman with Joined Hands* (oil on canvas, 90 × 71 cm, 1907). © Succession Picasso 2021.

meaning. In this way, contrast is increased in relation to the situation when the mouth and the eye would have other forms and other meanings (lack of common features).

Contrasts:

1. Left eye—right eye: the same meaning and shape and different brightness.
2. Right eye—lips: the same shape and brightness and different meaning.
3. Left side of the face and background have the same brightness, but different meanings and compose the form of a triangle.
4. Shadow on the left and hair on the right: the same shape and different meaning.
5. Continuation of the line of the nose: the left line becomes an eye and the right one an eyebrow.
6. Other brightness of symmetrical parts of the face.

In Figure 9.7, the woman's eye is located in the middle of the head form. It causes a strong connection of eye and head forms (additional common feature), while enhancing the features that differ (in our imagination and reality, the eye is not centrally located). The other eye has a completely different form than the eye in the middle of the head (a distinct feature). The common feature of the eyes is their meaning.

FIGURE 9.7 Picasso, *Repose* (oil on canvas, 81 × 65 cm, 1908). © Succession Picasso 2021.

Contrasts:

1. Right eye—head: the same centre of symmetry and other meaning.
2. Right eye—left eye: same meaning and other forms.
3. Hand and outline of light on the face and eyebrow have the same shape (arc) and size, but different meanings.
4. The whole body of a woman is a symmetrical form whose axis of symmetry runs as shown in the illustration. The axis of symmetry of a woman's body as a subject runs completely differently—almost vertically. So here we have a contrast between the form of the body and the abstract geometrical form, differing in the angle of inclination of the axis of symmetry, and at the same time, very strongly connected by the perfect overlapping.

Space in Cubism: one of the main achievements of Cubism was the separation of the structure of space in painting. The space itself is a very strong contrast to the flat canvas of the image if it is placed in an illusory manner on it. In addition, the space in images increases the number of types of contrasts in relation to flat representations (just as two-dimensional forms create more contrasts than one-dimensional ones). This is related to the greater amount of information contained in spatial representations. The introduction of a suggestive space to the image in Cubism has allowed the increase in the number of types of contrasts compared to flat-painted images, such as Gauguin's paintings. One such spatial image is *Landscape with a Bridge* (Figure 9.8). The strong structure of space is felt in it. Forms are not quite abstract; one can read a bridge, mountains, houses and a tree in the shape of a woman and the form of a lying woman overlapping the clearances of the bridge.

FIGURE 9.8 Picasso, *Landscape with a Bridge* (oil on canvas, 81 × 100 cm, 1909). © Succession Picasso 2021.

In analytical Cubism, the images are gradually deprived of the object. The space made of flat forms creates as if a relief or, as the cubists defined it, a short space. Such space in the picture seems more real (probable) than, for example, a perspective view. In those paintings in which the object is still visible, the relief (as an additional meaning and structure) overlaps the structure of the object (imposing the relief can be compared, for example, to the overlapping raster on images or rhyme structure in the poems). Of course, this is done at the expense of deformation and weakening of other structures, which are traditional spaces based on convergent perspectives and realistic objects. Partial weakening of these structures, which are already well known and recognizable and therefore constitute strongly distinctive wholes, can pay off if, after the imposition of new structures, the contrast increases. It is a matter of grasping the proportions of the impact of weakened (deformed) object structures and imposed (usually weaker) abstract structures. It seems that Cubism tried to study these proportions in various paintings.

In *Portrait of Ambroise Vollard* (Figure 9.9), we see a smooth transition from object to abstraction. Face forms are repeated in other places of the image, giving

FIGURE 9.9 Picasso, *Portrait of Ambroise Vollard* (oil on canvas, 92 × 65 cm, 1910). © Succession Picasso 2021.

FIGURE 9.10 Picasso, *The Accordionist* (oil on canvas, 130.2 × 89.5 cm, 1911). ©
Succession Picasso 2021.

them meaning. Just like in Impressionism, spots of one colour spread in the painting and then change to a different colour. Thus, one can talk about the spreading of
meanings, the gradual disappearance of them and the transition to abstract forms.

In Figure 9.10, the subject is not at all readable. If it is felt, it is evenly distributed
throughout the image. The breakdown of the subject in the pictures from that period
justifies the name Analytic Cubism.

While *Analitical Cubism* eliminated objects striving for abstraction, *Synthetic
Cubism* moved in the opposite direction. Gradually, in abstract analytic images,
simple object and geometrical structures begin to appear in the form of inscriptions, circles, parts of objects, e.g. a fragment of a guitar. These objects create a new
semantic structure in relation to the one that was previously broken and overlap it. In
this way, a previously broken object is recreated, e.g. a portrait of a woman reading
a book in a painting entitled *Bottle of Suze* (Figure 9.11).

FIGURE 9.11 Picasso, *Bottle of Suze* (charcoal, gouache and pasted paper, 64 × 50 cm, 1912). © Succession Picasso 2021.

This image is a synthesis of fragments of women, bottles, letters, newspapers and simple geometric forms. The form of a woman reading a book is being synthesized here. The introduction of new objective structures into the image increases its semantic content. These structures, when introduced to the abstract image have a strong common feature—objectivity, so it is necessary to strive for the greatest possible diversity of this objectivity. Hence the presence of such different structures as inscriptions, newspapers, drawings with coal and wallpaper.

Figure 9.12 depicts Picasso's painting entitled *Mandolin and Guitar* (1924), in which one can also discern a skull. The mandolin and the guitar resemble eyes, the perpendicular flower vase is the nose and the teeth are represented by a white rectangle at the bottom of the picture, with perpendicular black lines (gaps between the teeth) superimposed on it. The proof that the placement of the skull was not accidental is its outline visible against the sky, which can be part only of the skull. Just as in the preceding examples, the superimposition of visual structures reinforces here the contrast and the effects of all elements of the painting.

FIGURE 9.12   Picasso, *Mandolin and Guitar* (oil and sand on canvas, 140.6 × 200.2 cm, 1924). © Succession Picasso 2021.

Superimposition is the most powerful means for connecting one visual structure to another. It may be said that the common form of two different meanings is the strongest common feature that may be generated in connecting visual structures. Consequently, the more different the superimposed structures are and the more precisely they are superimposed, the greater contrast is created. An example of perfect superimposition is shown in Figure 9.13, where the form of a hare's head and that of a duck coincide precisely. A big contrast produces a striking effect. For the first time,

FIGURE 9.13   An example of perfect superimposition of two forms: the head of a hare and that of a duck.
Note: This work is in the public domain in its country of origin and in other countries and areas where the copyright term is the author's life plus 100 years or fewer.

the picture linking the rabbit with the duck was made at the end of the 19th century and was published in the pages of the German humour magazine. A little later in his research, it was taken into account by psychologist Joseph Jastrow. The drawing became famous after Ludwig Wittgenstein used it to illustrate the difference between seeing something "such as it is" and something "such as it seems to be". This example (although it was not by Picasso) was included as the most characteristic for overlapping forms/meanings.

In Picasso's painting depicting still life (Figure 9.14), we are also dealing with overlapping. You can see here the similarity of the jug with apples to the body of a woman: two apples at the top resemble a breast, the plate can symbolize a bra, the jug—shape of a woman, ear of the jug—a hand and two apples at the bottom—legs. The preserved character of traditional still life additionally strengthens the contrast here.

FIGURE 9.14   Picasso, *Still Life with Pitcher and Apples* (oil on canvas, 65 × 43.5 cm, 1919). © Succession Picasso 2021.

FIGURE 9.15   Picasso, *Women Running on a Beach* (oil on plywood, 34 × 42.5 cm, 1922). © Succession Picasso 2021.

In painting *Women Running on a Beach* (Figure 9.15), the form of running women overlaps the form of a "swan taking off for a flight", which with an "outstretched neck" (extended hand) runs on water, taking speed to float. The contrast increases here additionally by introducing heavy forms of female bodies, compared with the lightness of the bird.

Picasso was aware that the space of cubist paintings does not exhaust all formal possibilities and, at the same time, he painted, suggesting a great depth and lumpiness of forms. One such painting is *Women Dressing Her Hair* (Figure 9.16), in which the painter's idea of obtaining the greatest depth of space is clear. Let me remind you that applying space to a flat surface of the image and thus binding these two structures (we see space knowing that the image is flat) is a key contrast in painting.

A very important discovery of Cubism was the materialization of knowledge about a given object in the form of showing it simultaneously from several sides, more precisely: a structural juxtaposition of its most important visual features, so that they could interact simultaneously in direct perception. Of course, the strongest structures were used here, i.e. simple, familiar objects such as glasses, bottles, a guitar, a chair and, above all, human faces and bodies. These structures are most strongly coded in our imagination and have the most features. One of the many paintings in which Picasso synthesizes the features of an object that do not occur

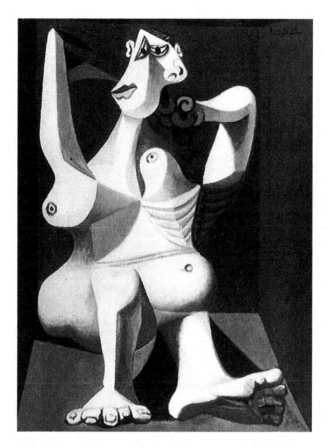

FIGURE 9.16   Picasso, *Women Dressing Her Hair* (oil on canvas, 130 × 97 cm, 1940).
© Succession Picasso 2021.

simultaneously (in reality perception) is *Weeping Women* (Figure 9.17). The face is a synthesis of front and profile view, which are the two strongest structures (the most distinct structures) of the face. In addition to these, there are overlapping structures/ forms of objects shown, although in reality, they would be obscured, e.g. we see hands, a handkerchief and a face in the same place. The overall composition resembles a cloud (hat), from which streams of rain (vertical lines) flow into the fields seen from above (women's clothing). This is one example of how to increase the contrast and strength of the image by superimposing many structures (semantic and formal).

   The pursuit of maximum contrast in the image through even greater autonomy of its elements, with an even their stronger binding, caused the search for new means and ways of combining them. One of the ways was to incorporate material reality into the image as a materialized illusion of space and object. Material objects appearing in the immediate vicinity of their illusion in the image created a new, high

FIGURE 9.17   Picasso, *Weeping Women* (oil on canvas, 60 × 49 cm, 1937). © Succession Picasso 2021.

contrast. This contrast was greater than the previous one, consisting in an indirect combination of reality and illusion. The next step was to put the ready-made objects in the image until the illusion was eliminated. The presence of the object in the image still makes it possible to create a contrast with its illusion, which existed in the imagination. Such contrasts include later *readymades of Marcel Duchamp.*

By materializing the forms of his paintings, Picasso made a continuous transition from image to sculpture and object. First by creating the illusion of space and matter, then using flat, ready-made structures in collages and finally creating flat sculptural structures and sculptures. In all these stages, there are strong, common features binding them together in a certain sequential whole. A characteristic example of the culmination of the road to the materialization of structures is *Head of a Bull* made of the handlebar and the saddle of a bicycle (Figure 9.18). What is common in Picasso's paintings is the juxtaposition of semantic organization with visual organization and the blurring of the boundary between them. Picasso did not give up any of these structures, because he cared above all about the richness of the means of expression. The movements in painting which separated these structures were Surrealism and Geometric Abstraction.

FIGURE 9.18 *Head of a Bull* (1943), assemblage of bicycle saddle and handlebars (33.5 × 43.5 × 19 cm). © Succession Picasso 2021.

Surrealism: a direction in art originated in 1924 in France, initially appearing only in literature, later in fine arts, film and theatre. This term was created in 1917 by Guillaume Apollinaire. In painting, the assumption of Surrealism was "visual expression of inner perception". The artists tried to create images that destroy the logical order of reality. Often these were grotesque visions from the border of reality, dream, fantasy and hallucination. Representatives of this trend in painting were: Salvador Dalí, Giorgio de Chirico, Max Ernst, Hans Arp, Marcel Duchamp, Francis Picabia and René Magritte. The painting of Hieronymus Bosch, who lived at the turn of the 15th and 16th centuries, is accepted as a significant inspiration for surrealist works. In addition, they benefited from the experience of Dadaism. In surreal paintings, the expression of visual formal means plays a secondary role. The main contrasts are created by the objective combinations of symbols and meanings in a surprising, unbelievable way.

Figure 9.19 shows a man in front of a mirror which reflects his back. The essence of the contrast here lies in the strong influence of common features: the identity of the man's view and his reflection, and the equally strong influence of different features: our experience of what should be reflected by the mirror (face and not the back) and the view of the man's back.

FIGURE 9.19   This is a Shutterstock photo with the description: "A man in front of mirror that reflect his back, surreal Magritte concept". (It could be Magritte's painting.)

In the Magritte painting *The Collective Invention* (1934, oil on canvas 73.5 × 97.5 cm, www.wikiart.org/en/rene-magritte/collective-invention-1934), on the beach, we see a fantastic creature with the head of a fish and the legs of a woman. The surprise is that, on the one hand, it seems familiar (common features) and, on the other, we have never seen anything like this before (different features). After a while, we realize that we are looking at an "inverted" mermaid. The high contrast (tension) results here from strong common features and differences between the observed object and remembered imaginations.

The Magritte painting *Personal Values* (1952, oil on canvas, 77.5 × 100 cm, https://www.renemagritte.org/personal-values.jsp) presents room with objects placed in it. These are furniture and familiar casual objects such as comb, soap, glass and match. The above description does not create contrast yet (it is probable—there are no differentiating features) and should be treated as a common feature (with our memory). Contrast appears here due to the enlargement of small objects like soap and comb to the size of the furniture (different features). A common feature, in addition to the presence of objects in the room, is the similarity of their size. An additional contrast (of a different quality) is created by the transparency introduced here (walls and wardrobes). Surrealistic images are also shown in Figure 9.20, and Figure 9.21.

Figure 9.20 shows a group of people in an African village. This is a postcard that Salvador Dalí received from Pablo Picasso in 1930. Once it is rotated 90 degrees to the right, a human face can be discerned in a pattern arrangement of dark and light spots. Inspired by the postcard, Dalí painted in 1935 an oil painting based on it, which he entitled *Visage Paranoïaque* (*Paranoiac Face*). Just as in the previous example, here we have an instance of superimposition of visual structures and their meanings. In Figure 9.3, the meaning of double-ness was superimposed on elements of the still life; here the face is superimposed on the structure of a rural landscape.

FIGURE 9.20 A postcard that Salvador Dalí received from Pablo Picasso in 1930. After rotating 90 degrees to the right, a human face may be discerned in the pattern of dark and light spots. © Succession Picasso 2021.

FIGURE 9.21 This is a Shutterstock photo with the description: "Famous Mae West room in Dalí's Theatre—Museum building, opened on September 28, 1974, and housing the largest collection of works by Salvador Dali". It was arranged according to: Mae West (Dalí, 1935, Gouache on newspaper, 31 × 17 cm).

As a result, each element and the whole gain a double meaning. The numbers of common and differentiating features increase. Therefore, the painting's contrast and its complexity increase. In addition, the contrast is reinforced by the fact that we are dealing with unprocessed photography in which the face is surprisingly clear.

Figure 9.21 shows a face made up of different objects, with the intention to juxtapose the most different structures. So, above all, the combination of space (the entrance door with a hair curtain, mouth and nose as sculptural forms placed on the floor, paintings as glasses and eyes—hung on the wall) with a flat view of these elements (in the form of a face), creates a strong contrast.

Geometric abstraction: it is a form of abstract art based on the use of geometric forms. Although the genre was popularized by avant-garde artists in the early 20th century, similar motifs have been used in art since ancient times. In Geometric Abstraction, the semantic side has been reduced completely. Important was only forms in the picture and only what influenced the viewer's eyesight. That is why abstract art is also called concrete art. Let's try to interpret some abstract images (Figure 9.22).

The plurality of art historians, curators and critics refers to *Black Square* as one of the seminal works of modern art and of abstract art in the Western painterly tradition generally.

FIGURE 9.22   Malevich, *Black Square* (oil on linen, 79.5 × 79.5 cm, 1915).

Note: This work is in the public domain in Russia according to article 1281 of the Civil Code of the Russian Federation (details). This work was originally published before January 1, 1925, and the known author of this work died before January 1, 1946, or died between January 1, 1946, and January 1, 1950, did not work during the Great Patriotic War (Eastern Front of World War II) and did not participate in it. This work is in the public domain in the United States because it was published before January 1, 1925.

The work is frequently invoked by critics, historians, curators, and artists as the "zero point of painting", referring to the painting's historical significance as a paraphrase of a number of comments Malevich made about The Black Square in letters to his colleagues and dealers:

- It is from zero, in zero, that the true movement of being begins
- Itransformed myself in the zero of form and emerged from nothing to creation, that is, to Suprematism, to the new realism in painting—to non-objective creation.
- Black Square is meant to evoke the experience of pure non-objectivity in the white emptiness of a liberated nothing.

(https://en.wikipedia.org/wiki/Black_Square_(painting))

The *Black Square* is therefore a context-aware (artistic and historical) work, expressing the end of an era and the beginning of a new one. In this sense, it is a common link—a contrast between traditional and abstract painting (abstract art). Common features with traditional painting are a kind of medium (picture on canvas) and a symbolic content, while the differentiating features are artistic awareness, resignation from the workshop skills and conceptuality. This work goes beyond not only depictive painting, but also painting in general in its conceptual nature.

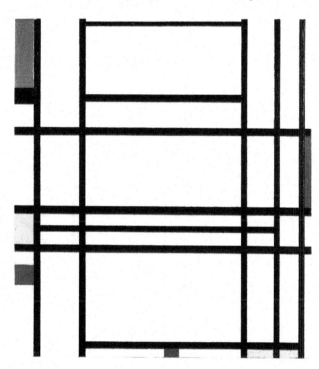

FIGURE 9.23 Mondrian, *Composition No. 10* (oil on canvas, 80 × 73 cm, 1942).
The author died in 1944, so this work is in the public domain in its country of origin and in other countries and areas where the copyright term is the author's life plus 75 years or fewer. This work is in the public domain in the United States because it was published (or registered with the U.S. Copyright Office) before January 1, 1925.

Piet Mondrian's painting is also conceptual in character, although it also has a strong connection with traditional painting as its definition. This definition consists of a few necessary formal means necessary to enable visual organization. These measures are: horizontal and vertical direction, three primary colours and greys.

Mondrian's painting *Composition No. 10* (Figure 9.23) clearly defines his radical but classical approach to the construction of horizontal and vertical lines, as Mondrian wrote, "constructed with awareness, but not with calculation, led by high intuition, and brought to harmony and rhythm" (Tosaki 2017). Examples that organize abstract geometric forms include two works below.

Figure 9.24 combines flat and spatial structures. The features of both structures have a visible cuboid in the lower left corner. The contrast that arises here is the result of a strong bonding of these structures.

Op-Art: it is a direction in graphics, fashion, applied art and painting, whose task is to influence the viewer's eye, not his intellect or emotions, using abstract combinations of forms giving geometrical optical illusions, light, dynamic and textural

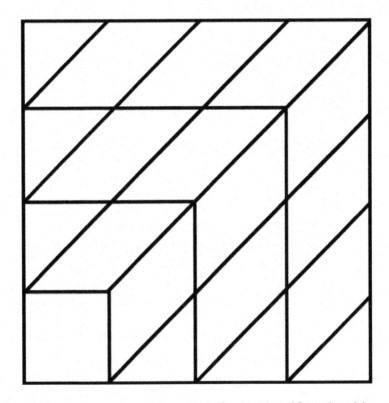

FIGURE 9.24 Stanowski, *Abstract Form* (1984). Combination of flat and spatial structure.

effects, aiming at creating the impression of depth and movement by deflecting the field of view. Op-Art can be considered a contrast to both depicting painting and geometric abstraction. Victor Vasarely and Maurits C. Escher are best-known representatives of this field.

In Vasarely's *Capella III* (Figure 9.25), there appears intangible circles of graduated degree of grey. It may be said that we observe a gradation of grey on a plane that we recognize as uniformly white. Thus, the perceived visual effect unites two opposing features: specific greyscale values, which are perceived optically, and the whiteness "perceived" by our consciousness. This work makes use of the so-called colour propagation effect, which consists in the colorization of background by the elements distributed on it.

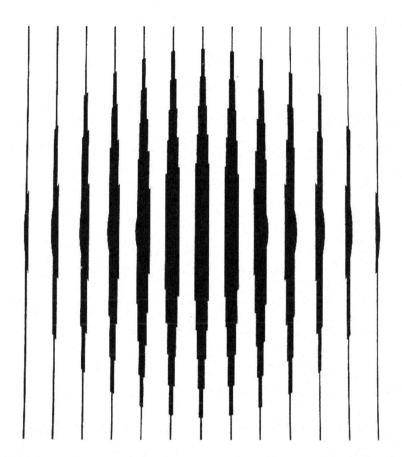

FIGURE 9.25   Vasarely, *Capella III* (1967). Intangible circles of graduated brightness of grey appear in this picture. We see a gradation of brightness on a plane that we recognize as uniformly white. © Vasarely Estate 2021.

Interesting contrast we can find in Maurits Cornelis Escher creation. His woodcut *Sky and Water* (https://en.wikipedia.org/wiki/Sky_and_Water_I) shows a pattern made of birds and fish that smoothly pass from one to another in such a way that the birds exactly fill the gaps between the fish and vice versa. A surprising effect is created by the following contrasts:

1. Birds—fish.
   Common features: the arrangement of fish and birds is symmetrical (two identical halves of parallelogram).
   Different features: meanings and brightness.
2. Birds and gaps between fish.
   Common features: common form and smooth transition between their meanings. Different features: meanings.
3. Fish and gaps between birds.
   Common features: common form and smooth transition between their meanings. Different features: meanings.
4. Parallelogram—background.
   Common features: overlapping the parallelogram form on the background, the rectangular form creates reverse symmetry, and half of the form is light and the other half is dark.

Different features: shape (parallelogram and rectangle) and meanings.

Another interesting Escher's example is his lithograph (https://en.wikipedia.org/wiki/Relativity_(M._C._Escher) which shows the interior designed for three perpendicular directions of gravity. The structure has seven stairways, and each stairway can be used by people who belong to two different gravity sources. This creates astonishing contrasts, such as in the top stairway, where two inhabitants use the same stairway in the same direction and on the same side (common features), but each using a different face of each step, and thus, one descends the stairway as the other climbs it (different features).

Conceptualism: the period of modernism mainly focused on the search for new formal means and continued the process of raising awareness about what art and artistic creativity are. Its last direction was Conceptualism, whose precursor is considered Marcel Duchamp.

In 1917, Duchamp exhibited his famous *Fountain*, that is, an ordinary (readymade) urinal (https://en.wikipedia.org/wiki/Fountain_(Duchamp)). The urinal was a contrast to the context of the whole art, primarily to its essential features/conditions, i.e. the aesthetics of an artwork and the necessity of its completely independent execution by the artist (differentiating features). A common feature was the context of an art gallery.

Figure 9.26 presents one of the most important works of conceptual art, titled *One and Three Chairs* (1965). It assembles a chair, a photograph of that chair and a definition of the chair, as three forms of the same concept. We have a contrast of different forms/objects of the same concept. The common feature is the concept of the chair, while the differentiating features are different forms of that concept. There is

FIGURE 9.26   Kosuth, *One and Three Chairs* (1965). Juxtaposition of a chair, a photograph of that chair and a definition of the chair as three forms of the same concept. © 2021 Joseph Kosuth / Artists Rights Society (ARS), New York.

some analogy with the contrast we encountered in Cézanne's still life (Figure 9.3), in which the concept of double-ness was superimposed on various objects.

Postmodernism: this describes movements which both arise from, and react against or reject, trends in modernism. Specific trends of modernism are formal purity, medium specificity, art autonomy, authenticity, universality, originality and revolutionary tendency, i.e. the avant-garde. It can also be understood as opposition to the concept of rational nature of culture and its linear development.

One of the first and most characteristic examples of postmodern art is the creative, Niki de Saint Phalle, a French-American sculptor, painter and filmmaker. She first received worldwide recognition for *Angry*, violent assemblages which had been shot by firearms. These evolved into *Nanas*, light-hearted, whimsical, colourful, large-scale sculptures of animals, monsters and female figures. An example is the sculpture *The Three Graces* (Niki de Saint Phalle, 1994; https://pl.pinterest.com/pin/776378423233560658/). The artwork presents three dancing women in colourful costumes. The work is purely decorative. It is difficult to find significant contrast values here, apart from a reference (reaction) to the analytical art of Conceptualism.

Another well-known and typical postmodern artist is Jeff Koons. His *Balloon Dogs* (www.jeffkoons.com/artwork/celebration/balloon-dog-0), like other works, have characteristic postmodern features: they are repetitive, kitschy, not reflective, not original (not made by the artist), perfect and commercial.

Trying to determine contrast in these and similar postmodern artworks, it would be difficult to find it in the artworks themselves. Their contrast should be considered in the context (of modernism), which is the base and reference for postmodern art.

FIGURE 9.27   Libera, *Lego. A Concentration Camp* (1996). The Auschwitz concentration camp built with Lego bricks. Courtesy of the artist and Raster Gallery, Warsaw.

An important direction of the postmodern period is also the so-called engaged art. An example of socially engaged art that raises reflections is the artwork of Zbigniew Libera, *Lego. A Concentration Camp* (Figure 9.27), showing Auschwitz concentration camp built of Lego bricks. On the model, we can see a fence, barracks where prisoners were kept, watchtowers and people participating in the roll call. The whole is a compact and symmetrical composition. Opposite meanings of the extermination camp and the child's innocent play are strongly compared. A strong contrast arises.

9.2   CONCEPTUAL ART AND ABSTRACTION: DECONSTRUCTED PAINTING

Taking a position in the discussion on contemporary art, I would like to present my view of art and the concept of painting based on my article published by Leonardo, MIT-Press (www.mitpressjournals.org/doi/abs/10.1162/leon_a_01859 (Stanowski 2020).

Rather than a theoretical treatise on existing ideas, this article should be understood as an account of this author's self-conscious intuitions resulting from the contemplation of developments in art that inspired a conception of art and of painting, exemplifying that conception. Those developments are outlined below. Following the analytical art of the 1960s and 1970s (Conceptualism) came the postmodernist turn and a loss of interest in deeper theoretical investigations. Artistic consciousness, which had such a key role before and in the era of Conceptualism, became less important. The use of new media to describe reality, communicate content (e.g. social content) or express emotions, reflecting largely the contribution of Joseph Beuys and Neo-Expressionism, was effected superficially, without taking into account a significant change brought by 20th-century art (including Conceptualism), which consisted in the identification of art with reality and of content with the formal element. While content was now given a greater role as a formal tool, it was also treated (in its referential aspect) in a traditional manner, as external to art, despite the fact that 20th-century art had sought to include in its remit all things extra-artistic, thus implying that art can be everything (every object). As Grzegorz Dziamski noted, following Boris Groys:

> Today everything may be art; everything may function as art, because art has liberated itself of all constraints, including the constraints of its own definition, and gained absolute freedom. Art became absolute, as Boris Groys says. It became absolute because it made anti-art a fully legitimate part of itself, and from that moment on, from the time anti-art was incorporated in the realm of art, it is not possible to either undermine or negate art, because even negation of art is art, as attested moreover by a long, almost century-old tradition, going as far back as the first readymades of Marcel Duchamp.
>
> **(Dziamski 2009: 7)**

Conceptualism completed the process of absorbing reality into art by including, in addition to material spheres (incorporated by earlier trends), such as the earth and the body, the creative process and even life, as well as thought, content and its referent (Kosuth 1991). Parallel to those changes, consciousness was altered, e.g. by Jacques Derrida's deconstruction, consisting of an internal reconstruction of familiar formal structures of meaning. The result is that when reality is considered in the context of art, art can be understood as reality itself rather than something existing alongside reality.

There is also a psychological aspect related to that process: the artistic personality perceives reality precisely as art (for example, in actions identifying life with art). The consequences of identifying art with reality go further. Today, when examining any object (of reality) in the context of art (as an artwork), it is necessary to recognize that such context comprises its entire reality (as art). Consequently, any reference/ meaning of the artwork also belongs to that context (which means that it is a formal artistic element), and since it is linked to the artwork, it also forms part of its formal tools. Hence, the postconceptualist period presents new types of formal elements, representing a synthesis of the formal element that existed before Conceptualism and its (then) meaning/reference (assuming no significant change in meanings in relation to the past). Such formal elements no longer have any external meaning/reference (since they have been internalized) relating to reality conceived as existing outside art. On the other hand, as a result of the equation of art with reality, the former has no longer any contact with the latter, and today we can deal with either art or reality, depending on which of these two dimensions we choose to be active in. By treating any object of reality as a formal element of art, we also turn all other objects of reality into formal objects of art, because for a given object to remain a formal element of art, it must be considered exclusively within the context of art. Therefore, any relationships between individual formal elements can only operate within the realm of art (as with relationships with the other formal elements). This view of art brings to mind the abstract art of the early 20th century, the essential aim of which was to shed its relations with reality. In *Cubism and Abstract Art*, Alfred Barr explained the meaning of the word *abstraction* as follows:

> The verb *to abstract* means *to draw out of or away from*. But the noun abstraction is something already drawn out of or away from—so much so that like a geometrical figure or an amorphous silhouette it may have no apparent relation to concrete reality.
>
> **(Barr 1936)**

Today, we also confront the severance of links between art and reality, albeit in a different way than in the case of geometric abstraction. Thus, in line with the above-cited definition, formal elements of art freed from any relationship with reality can be regarded as abstract, and the use of such elements may be described as "abstract art". The failure to take account of the identification of art with reality is attested by the referential nature of contemporary art, as well as by the views of art theorists who believe that only such art is possible. For example, Arthur Danto in *The Transfiguration of the Commonplace* stated that each artwork is (must be) about something, that it is a type of statement about reality (Danto 1981).

The referential nature (or commitment) of art introduces a division of the artwork into object and reference (meaning, content), differentiating the reference as a formal element external to the work (a meta-element). That distinction is all the stronger because the reference is a special (not visual) kind of formal element. Such division of the artwork is not conducive to unfettered creativity, which consists in the integration of any number of diverse (but nevertheless equal for creative purposes) formal elements. For instance, in Wilhelm Sasnal's *Untitled* (2009) (https://pl.pinterest.com/pin/206391595394275097/), a painting depicting tires on a beach; the object is the painting, while the reference is, for example, environmentalism. Instead of entering into play with other formal elements of the painting such as colours, shapes and arrangement, the reference (as a formal element) constitutes another and separate part of the work (to which the former elements are subordinated). In contrast, in such paintings as my *Last Supper* (Figure 9.28), formal elements are much less constrained and treated equally. If we agree that the referential nature of art is in line with the reigning paradigm (discernible to a lesser or greater extent in all works presented at major exhibitions such as *Documenta* in Kassel or the *Venice Biennale*), one should consider that this formula blocks unfettered creativity and artistic expression. Jan Verwoert expressed a similar concern (Verwoert 2005), discussing the need to conceptualize painting by reaching deeper into painting itself, its language, formal structure and history, in contrast to the current practice (conceptualization), which merely positions painting as one of the available media (committed to the expression of some content, e.g. social content). As an analogy of such painting, I would point to socially engaged painting in the 18th and 19th centuries (e.g. the paintings of Jacques-Louis David). At that time, such art was criticized by supporters of autonomous art because it neglected artistic values by serving some ideology. Yet, ideology could not be integral to an artwork in the past to the extent it can be at present. This is because today the reference (meaning, content) can play the same role as other formal means, such as colour, shape, space, photo and quotation, without disturbing the integrity of the artwork. Such a solution is indispensable given the long record of

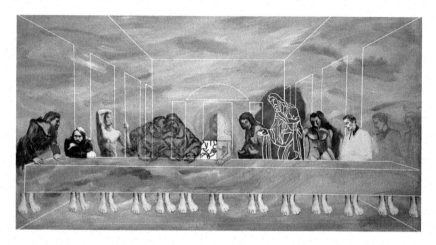

FIGURE 9.28 Stanowski, *Last Supper* (acrylic, photos, ink, charcoal, gold-paint on canvas, 170 × 90 cm, 1986/2002). Formal elements include: quotation, expression, geometry, realism, cubism, drawing, photography, charcoal, gold, colour, negative, complexity, poor visibility, multiplicity and perspective.

art's commitment to ideology (originated largely by Beuys) and the noticeable dearth and need for autonomous art as evidenced by, for instance, the title (*Viva Arte Viva*) and programme of the 2017 *Venice Biennale*.

HOW THE CHANGE MAY BE EFFECTED: AN EXAMPLE

Here I describe my own painting (which I have been pursuing since 1986) as an example of abstract art, conforming to the interpretation of abstraction outlined above. The formal elements of my paintings are the familiar formal elements of art, that is, those that became differentiated (achieved autonomy) in the course of the history of art (primarily in the 20th century). Because they are already differentiated and known (equipped with meanings attributed to them), they should be treated as new formal elements representing the synthesis of the form (visual/material element) and its meaning. I have described such paintings as pure because it also employs formal elements devoid of referents (since referents/meanings have been inducted into formal elements) or pure forms. I discussed this in a 1986 manifesto:

> Crisis of Art as Art: If we equate the crisis of art with the exhaustion of formal means of expression, that is if we agree that each structure of reality has already been a formal means, then this is a very positive development. The art that we currently practice is purer than ever before. At present, when all elements of reality may be considered formal elements, in engaging in artistic activity we deal exclusively with formal elements, or pure forms. In the process of creation, new pure forms are born out of pure forms; therefore, the creativity itself is a pure form—art. If this is so, then we must not invent new formal means, but on the contrary we need to take advantage of those already available. The more they are known, the purer such forms become.
>
> **(Stanowski 1986a)**

Examples of new formal elements are listed in the text *Pure Painting—Interpretation* (Stanowski 1986b):

The object of Pure Painting is the whole existing painting, just as reality is the object of existing painting. I consider the existing painting to be much wider than a collection of existing artworks, i.e. I consider it as all formal elements to be eligible for specific types, movements and styles of painting which in fact could represent all spheres of reality (it has become possible due to the expansion of painting in [the] 20th century). Pure Painting can be a synthesis of any existing formal elements. First of all, however, it tries to set together the most known elements, i.e. those that are most prominent in the whole area of painting. Here are some examples of them:

A. Formal elements distinguished by particular movements in painting:
   - Colour—most strongly distinguished by Impressionism.
   - Space and visual organization—by Cubism.
   - Geometrical forms and structures—by Geometric Abstraction.
   - Object—by Pop-Art.
   - Gesture—by Abstract Expression.
   - Objective references—by Surrealism.
   - Visual structures related to physiology of vision—by Op-Art.
B. Formal elements distinguished by individual artists:
   - Colours blue and gold—Yves Klein.
   - Line—Piero Manzoni.
C. Workshop-related structures:
   - Sketches, projects and notes.
   - Text—On Kawara.
   - Graphic techniques, drawing (pencil, charcoal, ink), watercolour, oil, acrylic and photography.
D. Abstract elements:
   - Inverted, exact, complex, large, small, double, coloured, unfinished and multiple.
E. From the point of view of the whole area of painting, the formal elements are both elements in different types, movements, styles as well as whole movements, types, styles that are distinguishable and visually recognizable, even in small fragments of images. These are more complex elements, covering wider formal areas, and qualitatively different from the elements themselves, i.e. elements of particular movements, types and styles of existing painting. Here we can include:
   - Styles of individual epochs, e.g. Gothic, Renaissance and Baroque.
   - Styles of particular movements, e.g. Impressionism, Realism and Cubism.
   - Styles of individual painters and quotations, e.g. Joan Miro and Victor Vasarely.
F. Various types of painting, e.g. Primitive Painting, Child Painting, Egyptian Painting and Graffiti.

What the Pure Painting is:

- Pure Painting is a tautology because it only refers to painting.

- Pure Painting uses familiar, existing formal languages—in this sense, Pure Painting is a metalanguage.
- Pure Painting is a pure form. Elements of Pure Painting are obtained by selecting specific structures of the existing painting. Selected structures/elements detached from their own context and placed in the context of Pure Painting lose their previous (utility) functions, like ready-made elements in the context of art.
- Pure Painting is the most abstract painting because it abstracts formal elements in a broader sense than abstracting from objectivity as existing abstract painting does. Pure painting also treats a specific object as a form abstracted from the context of objectivity (in existing painting) and represents this context (as a meaning) in Pure Painting; likewise it treats abstract elements, e.g. geometric forms.
- Pure Painting associating pure formal elements (visual part of existing formal elements together with their meanings, references and content) is pure creativity.
- Pure Painting is the result of not related to anything specific, an abstract necessity of creation.

The idea of Pure Painting is founded on the assumption that all important formal elements of painting are already known (and represent, in a sense, ready-made objects). Pictures are created here by choosing any formal element, e.g. portrait, and *rebuilding* it using other (known) formal elements such as colour, photography, direction, negative and brightness. This method resembles Derrida's deconstruction. The analogy is useful here because all formal elements (like words in a text) have meanings ascribed to them. For instance, in *Last Supper* (Figure 9.28), the quotation (of da Vinci's *The Last Supper*) has been subjected to deconstruction. The meanings associated with the visual formal elements include: quotation (of a well-known painting), expression (first man on the left), charcoal (a group of three people on the left side of Christ), photography (legs), sculpture (third man on the left), Cubism (third man on the right) and perspective (white lines). Each formal element may be both constitutive and deconstructed; all formal elements in Pure Painting are treated equally. The conception proposed here does not rule out the possibility of using (temporal) context to represent similar solutions, such as Neo-Expressionism or socially committed art. However, it treats them as individual formal elements (types of ready-made objects) employed to express an idea or a metaphor. Moreover, it offers an alternative that puts these ready-made objects to use as material for creating complex structures, thus restoring the possibility of composing (building)—as in music or Cubism, but on a higher (meta) level.

To further clarify the essence of this concept of art, it is helpful to describe its references. These references are general and as such testify to the autonomy of the paintings introduced here rather than to their referential nature:

1. When viewing the paintings (Figures 9.28–9.33) made in line with the proposed conception, we notice that the associated formal elements become differentiated (identifiable) and the creative process is conscious and

perceptible. This is how painting communicates the idea of creation (being a metaphor and an expression of creation). This point is discussed in the following fragment of a larger text titled *Creation and Expression of Creation*:

> I paint in such a way as to reveal the process of combining the formal elements. It seems to me that especially in the case of painting, where the creative process tends to be concealed, it could be stimulating to bring that process into the open. In my view, creativity is the deepest motivation for all activity today, as well as a necessity, regardless of whether our activity is truly innovative or only limited to mere subjective expression. When I realized that rather than tracing my own path, my work would have to follow one of the roads already traveled, I experienced it as a drama of the inability to attain self-fulfillment in our times. Later on, it occurred to me that instead of creating anything I can express the idea of artistic creation itself.
>
> **(Stanowski 1996)**

As examples of the disclosure of the creative process I should mention the paintings of Picasso and Arcimboldo, wherein the building and creation are most visible.

2. This form of painting represents the very definition of painting, because it defines all formal elements of painting. If we agree that all formal elements of art are also (in a sense) the formal elements of painting, the latter can also be regarded as the definition of art, as well as the definition/model of reality (in accordance with the idea that art superimposes itself on reality). I understand the painting of Mondrian, where painting is defined as vertical and horizontal direction and basic colours (black, white and grey), along similar lines. The model character of Mondrian's painting was noticed by many theoreticians, e.g. Y.-A. Bois in *Painting as Model* (Bois 1990).

One can tell a great deal about painting from a name/label. At first, I described my painting work as pure. Such designation seemed the most appropriate, but its association with purism in painting was uncalled for. Thus, I later began to use the term conceptual painting, since concepts were its most critical formal elements. That painting work represented, in my view, a synthesis of traditional painting and Conceptualism. However, that name subsequently became associated with a trend in painting, which to me had little to do with Conceptualism. The third label I considered for reasons outlined above was abstract painting. However, that term already refers to abstract painting of the early 20th century. Presently I am thinking about choosing the designation deconstructed painting, which has been kindly suggested to me, probably because it is a new term in the field of painting and says a lot about the concept of painting presented in this article.

EXAMPLES OF PAINTING

The (formal) content of this painting is a compilation of various meanings—formal elements defining painting as, among others, colour, perspective, transparency, quote (including its literary content), photography, perspective, coal and Cubism.

FIGURE 9.29   Stanowski, *Viewpoint* (acrylic, on canvas, 140 × 90 cm, 2018). The basic formal elements include: content (very popular today, tourist trip), perspective, colour, quotation, transparent, double and big (the sleeping Venus).

The composition and its elements are visible here. In this way, the creative process is revealed, which (through disclosure) becomes a metaphor of creativity.

Figure 9.29 shows a group of tourists watching the sea and sleeping Venus (quote from Giorgione) in the form of a cloud in the sky. The social aspect isolated here (content, reference) does not play a superior role, but is treated similarly to other formal elements appearing in the picture such as: perspective, quote, colour, duality, size, reversal, transparency, brightness, monochrome element, a surrealist element and an erotic element.

In Figure 9.30, the theme of the three graces, often appearing in art (in painting and sculpture), has been subjected to deconstruction. One of the formal elements next to, such as, quotation, drawing, colour, eroticism, geometry, transparency, multiplicity, painting style, negative and race is the content (literary): during the photo session, the woman (on the right) receives a message. This content does not dominate, but participates in a formal game along with other listed elements.

Self-portrait (Figure 9.31) was painted for an exhibition on the occasion of the Polish Independence Day (hence the white and red element of the picture). In addition to this content element, the picture also contains photos of the author (from various years) and a portrait painted realistically. Other formal elements are: space (painted and real-attached cube), plane (F16) recently purchased to defend the borders and a fixed cube (as an electoral casket).

Contrasts:

1. The whole creates a contrast with the portrait painted inside. The common feature is the face structure, a feature that differs in size and style.

FIGURE 9.30 Stanowski, *Three Graces* (acrylic on canvas, 140 × 110 cm, 2018). Formal elements here include: quotation (new), drawing, colour, eroticism, geometry, transparency, multiplicity, painting style, negative, race and content (during the photo session, the woman on the right receives a message).

2. Contrast of a painted portrait with photos. Common features: the same person; features that differ: size, quantity and medium.
3. The distances between photos decrease gradually (creating a perspective), but half of the photos are different. Common features: the same change in the distance between photos; features that differ: half of the photos are different.
4. The cubistically painted left side of the (whole) portrait contrasts with the cube being affixed. Common features: colour, shape and size; differing features: type of space (two and three-dimensional) and medium.
5. The airplane and the triangular shadow on the forehead create a contrast. Common feature: similar form; different feature: other meaning.

FIGURE 9.31   Stanowski, *Self-portrait* (acrylic, cardboard on canvas, 100 × 70 cm, 2019).

6. Red and white resembles the Polish flag. The painted portrait resembles an eagle placed on the flag. Similar forms and different meanings create contrast.

In Figure 9.32, the portrait of Mona Lisa is made here from tiny photos of pop-star Madonna, stuck to the canvas. There are three meanings of M/madonna here:

1. Mona Lisa as madonna (Mona Lisa is madonna, because in the Tuscan dialect she can be her equivalent).
2. Madonna as a media image of a contemporary American singer named Madonna Louise Ciccone.
3. Madonna as Maria of Nazareth, the mother of Jesus (who is entitled to the title of Madonna).

These distant meanings (differentiating features) are strongly connected by imposition (common feature). A strong contrast is created.

FIGURE 9.32 Stanowski, *Mona Lisa* (photos on canvas, 100 × 70 cm, 2001). Portrait of Mona Lisa is made here from tiny photos of pop-star Madonna, stuck to the canvas. Formal elements here include: quotation, drawing, photographs, size and multiplicity.

9.3 NON-VISUAL EXAMPLES OF CONTRAST

When contrast is understood as tension resulting from the impacts of common and differentiating features, it may be applied not only to visual perception but also to other types of perception, such as verbal perception.

Example 1: in Wiesława Szymborska's poem entitled *Portrait of a Woman* (Szymborska 1998), a contrast appears in almost every line.

> Portrait of a Woman.
> She must be a variety.
> Change so that nothing will change.
> It's easy, impossible, tough going, worth a shot. Her eyes are, as
>   required, deep, blue, grey, dark merry, full of pointless tears.

FIGURE 9.33 Stanowski, *Infinite* (acrylic on canvas, 100 × 100 cm, 2020). The painting presents various aspects of the infinite concept. It is a common/organizing formal element. Other formal elements are: quote, act, object, sign and colour.

> She sleeps with him as if she's first in line or the only one on earth.
> She'll bear him four children, no children, one.
> Naive, but gives the best advice.

Consider, for example, the following sentence (second line): *Change so that nothing will change.* Here we have several contrasts, the most important of which is the fragment: "nothing will change". It has two, mutually exclusive meanings; namely, the absolute sense (absolutely nothing will change, including the woman) and the colloquial one (the situation will remain stable, despite changes taking place in the woman). Thus, we have here a strong connection (by superimposition) of meanings; one meaning that rules out any change in the woman, and another one that allows for change to take place. This produces a strong contrast. We encounter a similar contrast in Socrates' statement: *I know that I know nothing.*

Example 2: large contrasts are present whenever something makes an impression on us. They can also be found in a brief statement or a short text containing a lot of information, such as an aphorism or a joke. Consider the following sentence: *Say not* *always what you know, but always know what to say* (Claudius). With a simple formal manipulation (reversing the word sequence) we can obtain a symmetrical juxtaposition of two important contradictory meanings. *Know what to say* means that we give some thought to what we say, while *say what you know* implies that one is careless about one's words. We have here a concise form that contains a lot of content; in other words, which is characterized by a strong compression of the information.

Contrasts:

1. Formal contrast resulting from a reversal of the word sequence (symmetry)
   Common features: same words
   Differentiating features: different sequence
2. Contrast of two contradictory meanings
   Common features: similar forms (two symmetrical halves).
   Differentiating features: contradictory meanings.
3. Contrast of quality, which resides in a form (a pattern of words) being composed of two parts, which are symmetrical, and of the content that is also divided in two parts, which are mutually contradictory.

Thus, there is a contrast between symmetry and contradiction.
Common features: the form consistent with the content.
Differentiating features: symmetry and contradiction.

4. Contrast of contrasts (1 and 2) consisting in the small formal contrast (1) producing a large contrast (2).

Common features: contrast (1) associated with words provides the form for the contrast of meanings (2).
Differentiating features: different size and quality of contrasts.

Example 3: *Sasha is wearing only one shoe, when he is met by Vania, who says: "Sasha, you've lost a shoe!" To which Sasha replies: "Not lost, but found!"* This brief, concise joke contains a large contrast that resides in a powerful juxtaposition of two contradictory meanings, i.e. Sasha's losing/finding a shoe. These events are connected by their common result, which is that Sasha has only one shoe.

Example 4: the contrasts discussed above affect us strongly (they are characterized by a strong compression of information). This is why we like them, remember them and share them with others. However, we come across smaller or bigger contrasts essentially all the time when we perceive them or create new structures. Take dialogue as an example. If we stop to think what *dialogue* actually entails, we realize that each time we say something, we try (make an effort) to ensure that every utterance of ours has as much in common as possible with the previous speaker's statement, while being as different from it as possible.

REFERENCES

Barr, H.A. 1936. *Cubism and Abstract Art*. New York: Catalog, Museum of Modern Art.
Bois, A.Y. 1990. *Painting as Model*. Cambridge: MIT Press.

Danto, A. 1981. *The Transfiguration of the Commonplace*. Cambridge, MA: Harvard University Press.

Dziamski, G. 2009. *Sztuka po końcu sztuki. Sztuka początku XXI wieku* [Art after End of Art. Art of 21th Century Beginning]. Poznań: Poznań University Press, 7.

Kosuth, J. 1991. *Art After Philosophy and After*. Collected Writings, 1966–1990. Edited by G. Guercio, foreword by Jean-François Lyotard. Cambridge, MA: MIT Press.

Stanowski, M. 1986a. *Crisis of Art. As Art*. Warsaw: Stodoła Gallery, Catalog.

Stanowski, M. 1986b. *Pure Painting – Interpretation*. Warsaw: Stodoła Gallery, Catalog.

Stanowski, M. 1996. *Creation and Expression of Creation*. Łódź: Bałucka Gallery, Catalog.

Stanowski, M. 2020. Conceptual art and abstraction: deconstructed painting. *Leonardo* 53(5): 485–491.

Szymborska, W. 1998. *Poems New and Collected*. San Diego, New York, London: A Harvest Book, Harcourt, INC.

Tatarkiewicz, W. 1980. *A History of Six Ideas. An Essay in Aesthetics*. Boston: Kluwer.

Tosaki, E. 2017. *Mondrian's Philosophy of Visual Rhythm*. New York: Springer, 110.

Verwoert, J. 2005. "Why Are Conceptual Artists Painting Again? Because They Think It's a Good Idea". *Afterall*, Antwerp, 12.

10 Interpretations of Existing Aesthetic Views

The theory of contrast presented here is general (not in the sense of generality, but in the sense of possessing a large amount of informational content), while also being specific, given that it may be applied to detailed analyses of aesthetic objects. An analogy can be drawn here to the rules for sketching objects, which are the same for a variety of objects, regardless of their general appearance or specific details. When the principle of contrast is recognized as the essential characteristic of impacts in general, it opens the way to analyzing everything, since everything we are aware of involves an interaction of some sort. In what follows, we use this principle to interpret major theories and definitions of beauty described by the history of aesthetics.

10.1 AESTHETIC VIEWS IN PHILOSOPHY

1. Little attention had been given to the notion of contrast so far. There are two items I've found in the existing literature. These are Whitehead's cosmology: *Process and Reality* (Whitehead 1978) and *Theory of Art: Inexhaustibility by Contrast* by D. Ross (Ross 1982), for which the concept of contrast, as for this investigation, was crucial.

In *Whitehead's cosmology*, contrast is the last (eighth) category of existence. He describes contrasts as:

> Modes of Synthesis of Entities in one Prehension or patterned Entities. The eighth category includes an indefinite progression of categories as we proceed from "contrasts" to "contrasts of contrasts" and on indefinitely to higher grades of contrasts.

This understanding of contrast is in line with our understanding of development as a synthesis of contrasting objects/structures (Chapter 7: "Contrast as Development"). The passage:

> That whatever is a datum for a feeling has a unity as felt thus the many components of a complex datum have a unity: this unity is a "contrast" of entities. In a sense this means that there are an endless number of categories of existence, since the synthesis of entities into a contrast in general produces a new existential type.

also talks about identifying contrast with development—*the synthesis of entities into a contrast in general produces a new existential type*—and about contrast as a feeling of unity—*many components of a complex datum have a unity, which is a contrast of entities.* Unity in multiplicity is also a well-known definition of beauty, which was authored by John Scotus Eriugena (9th century) and which gained considerable popularity in the 19th century (Tatarkiewicz 1980). A similar definition was for-mulated by Coleridge: *beauty is where the many, still seen as many, become one* (Ross 1982). This definition links (through contrast) Whitehead's cosmology with art. In our considerations, the feeling of unity can be understood as the result of a strong connection (by common features) of significantly different (distinguishing) components or the result of intense contrast. We do not experience such a sense of unity towards durable objects/wholes, even though they are so strongly integrated, because we do not see multiplicity in them. It is the multiplicity (in relation with unity) that causes the feeling of unity in contrast. According to this understanding, contrast is not a durable whole—an object (such as a brick) suitable for building more complex contrasts/objects. Contrasting objects then begin to combine into a durable whole when the contrast ceases to effect, because, with time, the different features are replaced by common ones (it was explained in the Chapter 7: "Contrast as Development"). Then we are dealing not with contrasts, but rather with new objects. These objects can be components of the next contrasts (syntheses), which, however, do not contain contrasts anymore but objects (that is, the wholes of which elements do not interact or have a weak interaction with our mind). Therefore, if one can speak about the hierarchy of objects, it is impossible to speak of a hierarchy of contrasts. If the feeling of unity in multiplicity is a contrast (where unity is not yet a durable whole, because its components are strongly distinguishable), then such a contrast cannot serve as material for higher degrees of integration (because it is not completely integrated itself). Therefore, the subsequent stages (of contrast) would be less and less integrated and contrast instead of increasing would be weaker and weaker. Taking this into account, I do not agree with Whitehead's thesis that

> the eighth category (contrasts) includes an indefinite progression of categories as we proceed from "contrasts" to "contrasts of contrasts" and on indefinitely to higher grades of contrasts,

in application to mental contrast which is associated with art. The error of this thesis can also be checked experimentally by trying to capture (in mind) such a hierarchical contrast. Example 2 (Section "Non-visual Examples of Contrast", Chapter 9) shows that it is not easy to capture even two levels of such a hierarchy, let alone three or more. Why Whitehead has chosen this particular understanding of contrast as *an indefinite progression of categories*? It seems that in his cosmology he wanted to combine art with the dialectic of Hegel. However, art, like contrast, cannot be hierarchized.

Ross's theory adapts the basic theses of Whitehead's cosmology to explain the fundamental issues of art. The advantage of this work is to draw attention to the diversity of contrasts and their significance for art. However, artistic value is defined here as the intensity of contrast, which (as in Whitehead's theory) results from capac-ity (of contrast) to produce higher levels of contrast:

> The most important feature of contrast is its capacity to produce level upon level of complex contrast upon contrast [...] If artistic value is intensity of contrast, what is important is how the contrast function and gain intensity. The capacity to promote

higher levels and richer complexities is the primary feature of our understanding of art, and a major contribution to the artistic importance of traditions and history. [...] It is the property that enables art, through intensity of contrast, to manifest inexhaustibility. [...] Ultimately, the value of art is that it manifests inexhaustibility, by enhancement and revelation.

This is the basic thesis of the theory with which I cannot agree.

2. Important conceptions unquestionably include the so-called *Great Theory of Beauty*, which was initiated by Pythagoreans, according to which, beauty resides in the selection of proportions and proper arrangement of parts, that is, it is based on size, quality, quantity and their interrelationship. In a more restricted version, it claimed that the proportion of parts constituting beauty may be expressed numerically; beauty resides only in objects where the proportion of parts corresponds to the ratio of simple numbers: 1:1, 1:2, 2:3 etc. (Vitruvius 1580). That theory prevailed until the 17th century, and no other theory in the history of aesthetics has had such lasting power. Its proponents included Aristotle (Aristotle 1937), Plato (Plato 1957), Saint Augustine, Dürer, Poussin and also Leibniz, who wrote: "Music charms us, although its beauty consists only in the agreement of numbers" and "The pleasures which sight finds in proportions are of the same nature; and those caused by the other senses amount to almost the same thing" (Leibniz 1714).

Interpretation:

This is the most abstract and objective among existing theories of beauty. Yet, if we attempted to use it to solve the riddle of the aesthetic attractiveness of the golden ratio (division), we would run into considerable difficulties considering that the golden ratio itself is not a ratio of simple numbers. It remains a mystery how the discoverers of the golden ratio (Pythagoreans) managed to reconcile its beauty with their theory. The Great Theory of Beauty, which explained to a considerable extent at the time what determines beauty, today appears too superficial and general.

3. Another important definition of beauty refers to the *shining through* of the soul, as in the case of *Plotinus—the beauty of proportions comes not so much from the proportions themselves, but rather from the soul which shines through these proportion—*and ideas, as in the case of Hegel—*beauty is the sensual shining through of the idea.*

Interpretation:

The *shining through* in question may be compared to, for example, the face that *shows through* on the photograph of an African village (Figure 9.20), the human skull (Figure 9.12) or the meaning of double-ness in the still life by Cézanne (Figure 9.3). Following these examples, *shining through* may be understood as the superimposition of meanings, forms or structures, which increases contrast, complexity and information compression.

4. In the 4th century, *Basil the Great* conceived the idea that beauty resides in relationship, not only among the parts of the object, but between the object and the human sight. This was one of the first attempts to take into account the relationship between the object and the subject.

Interpretation:

In our investigation, we noticed that structures contributing to the creation of contrast also include the structure of the observer's imagination. ~~and that~~ Contrasts emerge both among presently perceived structures (e.g. when we compare two objects) and between the presently perceived structure and the structure (when we look at one object) of the observer's imagination. The "relationship among the parts" should be understood here as the contrast among presently perceived structures, while the "relationship between the object and the human sight" as the contrast of the perceived structure and the structure of the observer's imagination.

5. The subjective nature of beauty was noted by *David Hume* (Hume 1896), who wrote: "beauty is no quality in things themselves; it exists merely in the mind which contemplates them; and each mind perceives a different beauty".

Interpretation:

The above conception of the structure of the observer's imagination as contributing to the creation of contrast also explains what subjectivity of aesthetic judgements consists in, as discussed in Chapter 13 "Contrast and Subjectivity".

6. *Beauty is the unity in diversity*: the creator of this theory is *Johannes Scotus Erigena* (9th century) This theory gained considerable popularity in the 19th century.

Interpretation:

Unity in diversity can be understood as the presence of a strong link (strong/ numerous common features) among numerous elements. This is nothing other than the definition of contrast and the above proposed intuitive criterion of complexity. Therefore, unity in diversity represents the intuitive understanding of large complexity and a strong contrast.

7. According to *Suzanne K. Langer* (emotionalist theory), artworks express primarily (broadly understood) human feelings (Langer 1957). A feeling is everything that can be felt. In the work of art, feelings are expressed symbolically and form an integral part of its structure.

By symbol Langer means everything that can be used to conceptualise something and define it in the abstract, e.g. a feeling. Thus, works of art are presentational symbols of feelings owing to the similarity among artistic elements, relations and forms, on the one hand, and forms of progressions of emotions, on the other.

(Dziemidok 2012)

Interpretation:

Sensation can be understood as the result of an impact. If artworks represent feelings, this means that they exert an impact in some way (create a contrast). There appear to be three types of contrasts: (1) mutual contrasts (defined here as relations) among (perceived) elements of the work of art; (2) contrasts between such (mutual) contrasts and forms of feeling progressions; and (3) contrasts between particular elements of the artwork and forms of feeling progressions (in our memory).

The value of this theory is that it draws attention to the semantic aspect of elements of the artwork, which can create relations, structures and contrasts, just like forms (shapes). By identifying the symbolic-emotional structure of the artwork, the latter can be related (similarity) to the structure of emotional progressions in our mind, thus also making it possible to analyze the contrast residing in such structures.

8. Artistic Formalism claims it is the formal structure that is constitutive and essential to a work of art. One of the leading representatives of Formalism is *Clive Bell*, the creator of the theory of "Significant Form" (Bell 1958). The significant form, according to Bell, is *lines and colours combined in a particular way, certain forms and relations of forms that stir our aesthetic emotions.*

Interpretation:

The concept of art proposed by Bell is too generic in that it fails to clarify in what way "certain forms, and relations of forms" come to stir our emotions.

9. A more specific description of aesthetic properties is provided by another representative of Formalism, *Monroe C. Beardsley.* Beardsley identifies three canonical qualities common to all aesthetic objects: unity, complexity and intensity.

Interpretation:

Unity should be understood as a strong common feature that connects various distinguishable elements of an artwork, hence also a strong contrast.

As our investigation has shown, complexity is also a contrast.

Intensity (of features and elements) may also be graduated. Hence, it can create structures and contrasts. Consequently, contrast is the common feature of all the properties mentioned.

10.2   AESTHETIC VIEWS IN PSYCHOLOGY

V.S. Ramachandran and William Hirstein (Ramachandran and Hirstein 1999) identified eight universal laws of artistic experience, determining preferences related to the perception of art. Let us discuss several of them.

10. *Peak Shift effect*: this effect consists in the amplification of characteristic features in, for example, caricatures or in the accentuation of the female

form in Indian images of women. The following example illustrates this
phenomenon: if a rat is rewarded for distinguishing between a rectangle
and a square, the rat will respond even more vigorously to a rectangle that
is more elongated than the original prototype used to train the animal.

Interpretation:
   The rat responds to the square/rectangle contrast. When one side of the rectangle
is made longer, this amplifies the contrast and consequently furthers the rat's mental
development, thus accelerating the rat's response to obtain the reward. Looking at a
caricature, we experience a contrast between our image of its object and that what
we see. The accentuation of characteristic features increases the evocative power of
the features common to the caricature and the observer's own appearance. At the
same time, deformation strengthens the impact of differentiating features. That is
why when looking at a caricature we perceive a greater contrast than when observing
a real face. In this case, development consists in our becoming better acquainted
with the visual characteristics of the caricature's object. Similar contrasts arise when
female features are accentuated (thin waist, broad hips and large breasts).

11. *Metaphor*: the effect of a metaphor is described here as the process of dis-
    covering a hidden relationship between different episodes, on the basis of
    which connection a new, more general category is created:

    Being able to see the hidden similarities between successive distinct episodes
    allows you to link or bind these episodes to create a single super-ordinate category,
    e.g., several viewer-centred representations of a chair are linked to form a viewer
    independent abstract representation of "chair-ness". Consequently, the discovery of
    similarities and the linking of superficially dissimilar events would lead to a limbic
    activation—in order to ensure that the process is rewarding. It is this basic mecha-
    nism that one taps into, whether with puns, poetry, or visual art.

Interpretation:
   The emergence of superordinate categories is nothing else but the creation of a new
structure as a result of the linking of contrasting structures. The new structure has
the common and differentiating features of the structures that have been connected.
Thus, there has been development here, and it is precisely this development that we
have preference for.

12. *Grouping*: as in Gestalt psychology (Wertheimer 1923), grouping is under-
    stood here as joining into groups of similar elements (that have common
    features, such as colour, shape and size).
    Grouping is a very basic principle. The different extra-striate visual areas
        may have evolved specifically to extract correlations in different
        domains (e.g. form, depth, colour), and discovering and linking mul-
        tiple features ("grouping") into unitary clusters—objects.
    This brings us to our second point. The very process of discovering correla-
        tions and of "binding" correlated features to create unitary objects or
        events must be reinforcing for the organism.

Interpretation:

Discovering connections between elements and binding them together is certainly an interesting and important activity for us. Let us try and consider why it is so, using the example of a Dalmatian dog photo provided by the authors (Figure 10.1).

At first glance, the illustration seems to include only dark splotches with different levels of density. After a while we notice a Dalmatian dog. This discovery has an effect on us, which means that we perceive a large contrast. Consider what structures have produced this contrast. Two structures have been combined: the structure of dark splotches (that do not denote anything) and the structure of a dog's image, that is, two structures that are differentiated by meaning. A powerful binding feature is the common dark splotches that belong to both structures. The effect of this contrast is further reinforced by the sudden emergence of the dog's image (the common and differentiating features are amplified). The common features are additionally strengthened by the fact that the Dalmatian does have dark spots in reality.

FIGURE 10.1   Initially seen as a jumble of splotches; once the Dalmatian is seen, its spots are grouped together—a pleasing effect, caused perhaps by the activation of the limbic system by the temporal lobe cortex.

Note: This work is in the public domain in its country of origin and other countries and areas where the copyright term is the author's life plus 100 years or fewer.

Therefore, the "pleasing effect" was created not so much as a result of the grouping of splotches but rather due to the strong effect of the contrast, i.e. a strong juxtaposition of differentiating features (we are intrigued by the fact that sometimes we see only splotches, and sometimes the image of a dog).

Consider another example of how the "pleasant sensation" of grouping is understood.

> Discovery of the dog and the linking of the dog-relevant splotches generates a pleasant "aha" sensation. In "colour space" the equivalent of this would be wearing a blue scarf with red flowers if you are wearing a red skirt; the perceptual grouping of the red flowers and your red skirt is aesthetically pleasing—as any fashion designer will tell you.

In the light of our investigation, aesthetic pleasure derives not from grouping (linking) red flowers on the scarf and on the red skirt as such, but rather from the effect of juxtaposed differences, that is, from the contrast of forms and meanings (the flowers and the skirt).

Common features: red colour.

Differentiating features: size, quantity and meaning.

13. *Symmetry*: the authors explain why symmetry is visually pleasing in the following way:

> Symmetry, of course, is also aesthetically pleasing as is well known to any Islamic artist (or indeed to any child looking through a kaleidoscope) and it is thought to be extracted very early in visual processing (Julesz 1971). Since most biologically important objects—such as predator, prey or mate are symmetrical, it may serve as an early-warning system to grab our attention to facilitate further processing of the symmetrical entity until it is fully recognised. As such, this principle complements the other laws described in this essay; it is geared towards discovering "interesting" object-like entities in the world.

Interpretation:

In accordance with our understanding, if symmetry is attractive, then it must produce a large contrast. The contrast is created here by symmetrical halves, which differ only in being the inverse of each other (ideal symmetry). Such contrast does not surprise us greatly because we are very familiar with it. Our preference for symmetry is due to the fact that it is not perfect. Owing to strong common features, symmetry is preserved even if it is partially deformed. Consequently, any differences or deviations from symmetry are strongly compared, and hence they create a large contrast. Since ideal symmetry is almost never present either in nature or in the arts (it is rare for the image of a face to be placed centrally, with both sides equally lit and with perfectly symmetrical features), symmetry is almost always accompanied by a large contrast. This is why we consider symmetry to be attractive.

14. Interpretation of basic Gestalt concepts

The basic premise and starting point for reflection in this work was the contrast of objects/structures which have common and differentiating features. It turned out that all the impacts of elements/structures and effects of these impacts can be reduced to the relationship of their features (common and differentiating). Such unification of perceptual experience allowed to see these effects in a new, abstract light, enabling their overall analysis and understanding. Let's try to take advantage of these conclusions for the interpretation of the main principles of Gestalt psychology. After over hundred years Gestalt theory became well known and present in many studies, so detailed description is not necessary here. Therefore let's concentrate on the basic concepts. According to Austrian philosopher Christian von Ehrenfels, the term "Gestalt" applies to perceptual unit formation and is characterized by two criteria: superadditivity and transposability (Ehrenfels 1890).

Superadditivity: this denotes that the whole is different from (or more than) the sum of its parts. Why is it like that? This question has not been answered yet.

Interpretation:

It appears from our investigations that the elements combined together into one whole have more features in common than when they are dispersed. These extra features make the whole different from (or more than) the sum of its parts. For example, in the structure of the circle, elements include features related to their arrangement: collinearity, equal curvature of the formed lines, equal distance from the circle centre and the same position of elements against each other.

In the structure of the square, the elements placed in the corners have an additional feature of equal distance from the other apices, and also the straight lines routed through the elements and their neighbours create right angles.

The fact that our mind distinguishes wholes can be explained here by the stronger association of their elements. A strong association also attracts differentiating features of the elements in the whole, thus increasing the contrast.

Let's consider two examples of superadditivity:

1. Superadditivity was illustrated by Wertheimer's phi motion:
   Two orthogonal lines presented briefly in the proper sequence will show phi motion (pure motion without object displacement) or appear as a single bar moving through a right angle (optimal motion). The perceived movement, including its direction and speed, cannot be reduced to the two static line events.
   An experiment showed that above a certain threshold value (200 ms), observers saw the two lines in succession. With much shorter intervals (30 ms), the two lines appeared to flash simultaneously. At the optimal stage (60 ms), observers perceived a motion that could not be distinguished from real motion (Wertheimer 1912).

Interpretation:

The illusion of motion (i.e. an irreducible whole) is formed here at an appropriate frequency of changes, which is similar to the frequency resolution in the human eye, or about 70 ms or less (Athanassios 2004), that is, when the components of the whole have more in common with the observer.

2. Another well-known example of superadditivity is a grey ring that is placed on ground that is half red and half green.

As long as the ring is perceived as a whole, it looks uniformly grey (Koffka 1935). However, if the two halves are separated by a thin border, a simultaneous colour contrast between the red and green hemifields induces a distinct greenish and reddish colour in two semicircles. Koffka concluded that an intact, unified figure (Gestalt) will look uniform, while the two semicircles produced by the same stimulus will look different. Thus, the whole has properties that are different from those of its parts.

Interpretation:
The fact that the whole has a uniform colour here is due to the strong binding with common features of its elements, which is so strong that we cannot distinguish them.

Owing to this union, the elements come into relation (similarity) with each other stronger than with the background. When they are separated (they have less in common), they enter into a relationship with the background and get colours.

Transposition: the second Ehrenfels criterion, transposition, implies that the whole is preserved even if there are large changes to its components. What counts are the relations between stimuli rather than the specific stimulus attributes. A square may be small or large, black or coloured, outline or surface or fully delineated or just defined by its apices. As long as there are four right angles connected by equilateral sides, it is a square.

Interpretation:
The strong connection of elements joined together (their strong features in common) causes an increased stability of the whole perception, because it is harder to break a stronger connection. Even when it is significantly weakened, the whole can still be recognized.

Prägnanztendenz: a key assumption of Gestalt psychology is that precepts organize themselves according to the principle of greatest Prägnanz, i.e. in the simplest, most regular and balanced manner possible, under the prevailing stimulus conditions.

Wertheimer (Wertheimer 1923) proposed that this equilibrium expresses itself in the Prägnanztendenz, or the tendency towards a "good" Gestalt. The term implies that the simplest, most regular and balanced organization "wins" in our perception.

To account for Prägnanz, the Gestaltists assumed a number of autochthonous (i.e. inherent) factors responsible for grouping and figure-ground segregation. These factors determine the way in which we see.

Interpretation:
Simple forms, regular and balanced (called "Good Gestalt"), are characterized by the fact that their components have strongest connections (as in an example of the circle above). Organizing our perceptions in accordance with those forms could be understood as follows: if looking at different distinguishable elements, we come across an item belonging to the whole; our perceptions will follow the next elements

belonging to the whole, because they are the most similar to them. As a result, the whole will be distinguished.

Grouping factors: a central issue of the Gestalt approach to perception is the distinction between figure and ground. The question of how we manage to parse a large stimulus field into figure and ground goes back to the Gestalt psychologists' proposal that figures emerge on a ground due to the so-called grouping factors (Wertheimer 1923), which are:

- Symmetry: if faced with symmetrical and non-symmetrical stimuli, perception follows symmetry as a figural organization principle. For example, spaces that are delineated by wavy, mirror-symmetric contours are perceived as figure and asymmetrical spaces as ground.
- Parallelism: similarly, undulating lines that are parallel and maintain their width achieve the status of figure, whereas their nonparallel interspaces are delegated the role of ground.
- Smooth (or "good") continuation: collinear stimulus parts tend to be linked together, whereas parts exhibiting sharp bends or corners are not. This observation calls for neurons sensitive to collinearity.
- Closure: a closed stimulus is more readily organized into a figure than an open one.

Closure also manifests itself in a tendency to complete perceptually a partly occluded object.

- Proximity: all other factors being equal, closely adjacent stimuli are more likely to be grouped into perceptual units than are stimuli that are farther apart.
- Similarity: stimuli sharing the same brightness or colour are more likely to be grouped than dissimilar stimuli. The same applies to size, shape and orientation as well as texture and depth.
- Commonfate: stimuli that move simultaneously at the same speed and approximately in the same direction are seen as a group. This factor, commonfate, ties together stimuli that are widely distributed in the visual field, producing the perception of coherent motion.

Interpretation:

In the light of our considerations these grouping factors could be regarded as different types of generally understood similarity (common features). This similarity (by definition) attracts similar elements and affects the figures (wholes) emerging on a ground.

- Symmetry: similarity of position and shape.
- Parallelism: similarity of direction.
- Smoothness: similarity of forms in places where they connect.

- Closure: similarity consisting in all elements that have a similar location to the neighbouring members.
- Proximity: similarity of position.
- Similarity: similarity in the narrower sense (purely visual).
- Commonfate: similarity of repetition.

More similarities, also important, could be added here:

- Similarity of appearance—standing apart.
- Similarity of spatiality.
- Similarity of styles.
- Similarity of complexity.
- Similarity of multiplicity.
- Similarity of reversal.

Types of visual similarities could be multiplied here. However, we need to keep in mind that other types of similarities frequently occur also in other domains.

The use of the general notion of similarity (common features) can help unify the field of perception and permit the application of the concept of contrast, understood as interaction between common and differentiating features.

REFERENCES

Aristotle. 1937. *The Works.* Oxford: W.D. Ross.

Athanassios, R. 2004. *Cognitive Penetrability of Perception: Attention, Action, Strategies, and Bottom-Up Constraints.* New York, Nova Science Pub Inc, 199.

Bell, C. 1958. *Art.* New York, Capricorn Books, 28.

Dziemidok, B. 2012. *Główne Kontrowersje Estetyki Współczesnej* [The Main Controversy of Contemporary Aesthetics]. Warsaw: PWN.

Ehrenfels, C. 1890. *Uber Gestaltqualitaten, Yschr. miss. Philos.14*: 249–292. Translation in Foundations of Gestalt Theory (B. Smith ed.). Munich: Philosophia-Verlag, 82–120.

Eriugena, J.S. *De divisione naturae* (9th Century). Migne. P. L. v. 35.

Hume, D. 1896. *A Treatise of Human Nature.* London: Clarendon Press.

Julesz, B. 1971. *Foundations of Cyclopean Perception.* Chicago, IL: Chicago University Press.

Koffka, K. 1935. *Principles of Gestalt Psychology.* New York: Harcourt, Brace.

Langer, S. 1957. *Problems of Art.* New York, Scribner, 15.

Leibniz, G. 1714. Principles of nature and of grace based on reason. *Philosophical Papers* 2: 1033–1043.

Plato. 1957. *Faidros,Fileb, Ion.* Warsaw: PWN.

Ramachandran, V.S. & Hirstein, W. 1999. The science of art. *Journal of Consciousness Studies* 6(6–7): 15–51.

Ross, S.D. 1982. *A Theory of Art: Inexhaustibility by Contrast.* New York: State University of New York.

Tatarkiewicz, W. 1980. *A History of Six Ideas. An Essay in Aesthetics.* Boston: Kluwer.

Vitruvius, M.P. 1807. *De Architectura* [The Architecture]. Leipzig: Schneider.

Wertheimer, M. 1912. Experimentelle Studien über das Sehen von Bewegung. *Zeitschrift für Psychologie* 61: 161–265.

Wertheimer, M. 1923. Untersuchungen zur Lehre von der Gestalt, 11. *Psychologische Forschung* 4: 301–350.

Whitehead, A.N. 1978. *Process and Reality.* New York: A Division of Macmillan Publishing Co, Inc.

11 Contrast and Colour

11.1 ANALYSIS OF COLOUR

The existing extensive knowledge about colour (which is generally known and available) says little about what is most important from an aesthetic point of view, i.e. about the reasons for the visual attractiveness of colour combinations, and is limited to the formulation of several principles of harmony with which the attractiveness/pleasure of perceiving colour combinations is identified (www.colormatters.com/color-and-design/basic-color-theory):

> In visual experiences, harmony is something that is pleasing to the eye. It engages the viewer and it creates an inner sense of order, a balance in the visual experience. When something is not harmonious, it's either boring or chaotic. At one extreme is a visual experience that is so bland that the viewer is not engaged. The human brain will reject under-stimulating information. At the other extreme is a visual experience that is so overdone, so chaotic that the viewer can't stand to look at it. The human brain rejects what it cannot organize, what it cannot understand. The visual task requires that we present a logical structure. Colour harmony delivers visual interest and a sense of order. In summary, extreme unity leads to under-stimulation, extreme complexity leads to over-stimulation. Harmony is a dynamic equilibrium. The basic theories for harmony are:
>
> The basic theories for harmony are:
>
> 1. A colour scheme based on analogous colours: Analogous colours are any three colours which are side by side on a 12-part colour wheel, such as yellow-green, yellow, and yellow-orange. Usually one of the three colours predominates.
> 2. A colour scheme based on complementary colours: Complementary colours are any two colours which are directly opposite each other, such as red and green and red-purple and yellow-green. These opposing colours create maximum contrast and maximum stability.
> 3. A colour scheme based on nature: Nature provides a perfect departure point for colour harmony.

Agreeing with these formulas, which were specified on the basis of experience, we would also like to understand them, i.e. find a broader rule for them. Let's check if they are covered by our contrast principle, according to which these colours contrast more strongly (i.e. their combination is visually more attractive), which have more common and differentiating features (while common features decide about the possibility of contrast, assuming that the colours are distinguishable).

1. The first rule says that the strongest contrasts create similar colours ("which are side by side"), i.e. those that have more common features (which is consistent with the principle of contrast).

2. The second principle says that the strongest contrast is created by complementary colours. Complementary colours, although are most different, also have an additional common feature, which consists in the fact that if we mix them, they create whiteness.
3. Colours based on nature have strong common features because they occur in nature next to each other. Thus, they create a strong contrast. Another contrast that occurs here results from the similarity of objects in nature (tree) and artificial objects (painted tree). Similar colours strengthen this contrast. This contrast, although it does not directly affect colours (but objects, forms), also increases contrast of colours, because these contrasts are perceived jointly.

In addition to the features considered above, i.e. hues, colours have also brightness and saturation, which also participate in contrasts. One should also take into account the colour features resulting from assigning them to objects and forms. If different colours have similar objects/forms (e.g. in Figure 11.17), they create a greater contrast than the same colours in objects which have weak common features.

I remember that for many years, I was impressed by the impressionists and colour in painting, and it took me a long time to search for universal rules for combining colours, which could possibly be practically used in painting. Both academic knowledge and existing literature did not give a satisfactory answer. The general opinion was that while formal measures such as space, shape and proportions could be the subject of analysis, in the case of colour, it was possible to rely only on intuition and experience. This was also confirmed by the lack of positive results in my own research. However, I returned to the subject after understanding the essence of visual interactions and formulating the principle/definition of contrast, which turned out to be so universal that I decided to check whether it could be used to analyze colour interactions, as in the case of analyses of other formal means such as shapes, size and meaning. It turned out that the combination of colours is also subject to the principle of contrast, which in this case also is an effective tool/method for analysis. To determine the contrast of colours combination, we would have to know their features. All colour systems are based on three parameters perceived by man as separate qualities: hue, brightness and saturation.

Hue: in these systems, hue is the result of mixing several of the basic colours in the spectrum (Figure 11.1), which the human eye feels as clearly different from the others. These hues have their names, and intermediate hues are defined as the percentage share of neighbouring primary colours.

FIGURE 11.1   Several colours selected from the spectrum: from red to violet.

Brightness: it is a feature of colour understood intuitively, depending on the amount of light (the amplitude of the wave), and it means the intensity of the colour. Its photometric measure is called luminance. The brightness impression is only readable in relation to the same colour. The above-mentioned samples of different colours have the same brightness, although we involuntarily consider the yellow sample as "brighter" than the green one.

FIGURE 11.2 Samples of colours with the same red hue and different brightness.

The appearance of brightness is quite complex. In the red colour samples shown in Figure 11.2, the sample on the right (black) means complete lack of light (darkness), subsequent samples are of more and more intense red light, the middle sample is red light with full brightness, and subsequent lightening stages are created as a result of adding to the red colour the other two components of white light—green and blue (GB). The gradual addition of these components brings the proportions of colours closer to the balance, which is white.

Saturation: the third colour parameter is saturation, expressing the purity of colour. The impression of saturation is intuitively legible with reference to colours of the same hue and brightness. The sample on the left shows the red hue in full saturation. The sample on the right shows the hue of the achromatic colour (grey) with the same brightness. It is a colour consisting of three RGB (red, green and blue) components. The impression of changing the saturation with the same brightness of colour is created by replacing a part of the red light with the right amount of the other two components—GB. As a result, the two components GB and the equal part of the R component give the achromatic colour (grey), which "stains" the pure red hue. The degree of saturation is therefore the colour distance from the grey with the same brightness (in the selected coordinate system) (Figure 11.3).

FIGURE 11.3 Samples of colours with the same hue and brightness, but with different saturation.

Colour is therefore a psychophysical phenomenon defined by three parameters, which a person perceives as separate and gradual qualities: hue, brightness and saturation. In addition, each colour also has a form (shape, size etc.) that always accompanies colour as well as meaning (symbolic)—attributed to colours from antiquity. For example, the ancient Egyptians attached great importance to colours of the sun, which were used to denote a man, his relation to the soul, body and earth. It was believed that the colour of the rays comes from God. In ancient China, the gold was of exceptional importance, and it was intended exclusively for the emperor. Thanks to numerous archaeological discoveries, we know that the Romans liked red, the colour of power and privileges, and the Greeks decorated their robes, artworks and houses with dark green and various shades of blue. We usually associate green with nature: trees, grass, landscape and peace; red colour with fire, blood, love, flowers and warning; blue with sky, water, cold etc.

All of the above-mentioned colour features come into relation (create contrasts) in colour combinations that can be analyzed like other visual structures. For our needs to show the operation of the principle of contrast, however, we do not need to use all these features, but to simplify the analysis, we will limit the number to four: hue, brightness, saturation and size. According to earlier findings, the highest contrast/complexity will be created by colours that have the most common and differentiating features. With the combination of two colours, if we assume the saturation and the same brightness, the greatest contrast is created by the complementary colours, that is, lying on the opposite side of the colour wheel. In practice, with a combination of two colours, to find the best result, it is not so difficult, i.e. having given a colour, we can match it so that the combination is liked (maximum contrast). It is far more difficult to compare three colours, because the number of combinations of features is already so large that it is possible to check only a very small part of their combinations. However, we can facilitate this task using knowledge about contrast. Below are some examples of triple and double combinations and we will analyze their contrasts similarly as in the case of abstract structures and counting common and differentiating features. It should be noted, however, that this analysis only approximates/supports the assessment of the strength of contrast or the attractiveness of the combination. Knowing the number of features, the strength of their impact, however, we must estimate intuitively.

ANALYSIS OF COLOUR COMBINATIONS

In Figure 11.4, each of the circles 1, 2 and 3 has a different colour, brightness and size. Common features are missing (shape and saturation is not taken into account because it is the same in all circles).

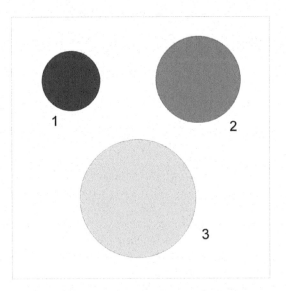

FIGURE 11.4 Each circle has a different hue, brightness and size. Common features are missing, and the contrast is small.

Common features: 0.
Differentiating features: 3 colours, 3 sizes and 3 types of brightness.
Total: 9 features.

Because there are no common features (weak connection), the contrast is small.

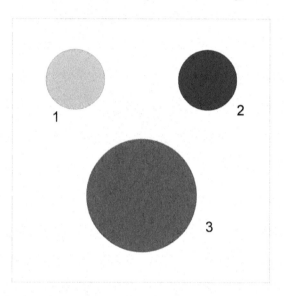

FIGURE 11.5 Elements 1 and 2 are related by size, elements 1 and 3 with hue and elements 2 and 3 with brightness.

In Figure 11.5, elements 1 and 2 are related by size, elements 1 and 3 by hue and elements 2 and 3 by brightness. Thanks to these relationships (common features), the contrast is greater: the colour, brightness and size are more closely compared.

Common features: size (1–2), hue (1–3) and brightness (2–3).
Differing features: size (1–3), size (2–3), hue (1–2), hue (2–3), brightness (1–2) and brightness (1–3).
Total: 9 features.

In Figure 11.6, the size similarity of elements 1 and 2 from Figure 11.5 has been replaced by their proximity.

Common features: proximity (1–2), colour (1–3) and brightness (2–3).
Features that differ: proximity (1–3 and 1–2), proximity (2–3 and 1–2), colour (1–2), hue (2–3), brightness (1–2) and brightness (1–3).
Total: 9 features.

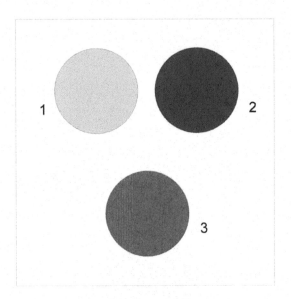

FIGURE 11.6   Circles 1–2 connect proximity, circles 1–3 colour and circles 2–3 brightness.

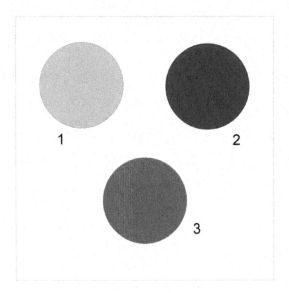

FIGURE 11.7   Colours 1 and 2 have bigger saturation than colour 3, colours 1–3 have similar hue, colours 2–3 have similar brightness.

In Figure 11.7, the size similarity of elements 1 and 2 from Figure 11.5 is replaced by a similar saturation of colours (colours 1 and 2 have a higher saturation than colour 3).

Common features: saturation (1–2), hue (1–3) and brightness (2–3).
Differing features: saturation (1–3), saturation (2–3), hue (1–2), hue (2–3), brightness (1–2) and brightness (1–3).
Total: 9 features.

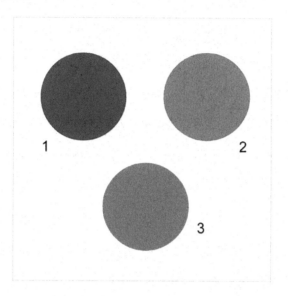

FIGURE 11.8 Three different colours have hidden relationships (common feature): if we mix red with green, we will get grey colour (3).

In Figure 11.8, three different colours have a hidden relationship (common feature): if we mix red with green, a grey colour will appear.

Common features: saturation (1–2), brightness (1–3), brightness (2–3), brightness (1–2) and hidden relationship (1, 2, 3).
Features that differ: saturation (1–3), saturation (2–3), hue (1–2), hue (2–3) and hue (1–3).
Total: 10 features.

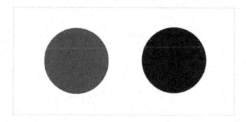

FIGURE 11.9 The red colour is combined with neutral colour—black. With the lack of common features, the contrast is small.

In Figure 11.9, the red colour is combined with the neutral colour (black).

Common features: none.
Differing features: saturation, hue and brightness.
Total: 3 features, no common features, small contrast.

FIGURE 11.10   Colour black from Figure 11.9 was broken with green and the contrast increased.

In Figure 11.10, black from Figure 11.19 was broken with green (some green was added to black), and the contrast increased.

Common features: the hidden relationship between red and green admixture (red and green are complementary colours).
Differentiating features: hue, saturation and brightness.
Total: 4 features.

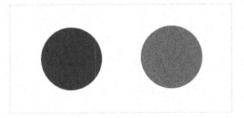

FIGURE 11.11   The green colour contains an admixture of red, and the red colour an admixture of green (they are broken). Although the colours are less intense here (lower saturation), they seem more interesting. This is because the colours have more features.

In Figure 11.11, the green colour contains an admixture of red, and the red colour—of green (they are broken). Although the colours are less intense here (less saturation) than in Figure 11.18, they seem more interesting. This is because the colours have more features here.

Common features: brightness, saturation and colours breaking.
Differing features: hue
Total: 4 features.

FIGURE 11.12 In the figure, we can see the colour red broken with green and green without admixture.

In Figure 11.12, we have red colour broken with green and clean green colour. Although the green colour has fewer features here than in Figure 11.11, in combination with a broken red, an additional saturation feature is created (resulting from the difference in saturation of both elements) in relation to Figure 11.11. The contrast does not decrease.

Common features: brightness and admixture of green.
Differing features: hue and saturation.
Total: 4 features.

FIGURE 11.13 There are two clean complementary colours: red and green.

Figure 11.13 shows two clean complementary colours: red and green.

Common features: brightness, saturation and hidden relationship (red and green are complementary colours).
Differing features: hue.
Total: 4 features.

As we know, the complementary colours create the greatest contrast. Although they differ significantly, they also have a hidden relationship: when overlapped, they create white light. This relationship is important for the physiology of colour vision. The retina receptors responsible for seeing colours are connected in pairs, for example, receptors responsible for seeing red light in a specific area of the retina with receptors responsible for seeing green light in the same area of the retina. All these receptors simultaneously send their information to the collective cell. When white light falls on this area (which consists of both red and green light), red and green receptors are stimulated to the same extent, which causes the collecting cell to send information to the brain that it "sees" in a given area of white light. If a red light falls on a given area, the action of the red light receptors outweighs the green one and the collecting cell "tells" the brain that it "sees" the red light. If now white light falls back to this area of the retina (i.e. theoretically red and green receptors should react with the same force), then it will turn out that the red receptors are "exhausted"— they send weaker signals than green receptors. Ultimately, the collecting cell sends a signal to the brain that it sees green light. If, however, instead of white, the green light falls on the area, then the red light receptors does not participate in its transmission (they are relieved), which facilitates the process of perception. So if we place complementary colours close to each other, their perception is more economical for our physiology of perception, which has a beneficial effect on our aesthetic feelings. This explains the important reason why we like paintings of impressionists so much.

Colours, in addition to creating contrasts with each other, can create contrasts performing the function of organizing visual objects, thus increasing the number of distinctive structures. In Figure 11.14, red colour forms a straight line, blue—a parallelogram, green—an arrow and yellow—three double elements. Without colours, these structures would be unnoticeable.

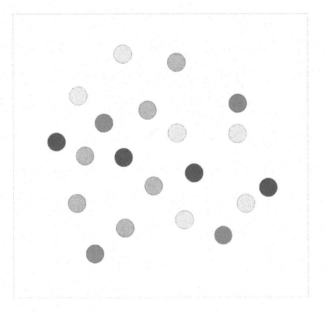

FIGURE 11.14 Distinguishing (with colours) structures of circles: red colour forms a straight line, blue—a parallelogram, green—an arrow and yellow—three double elements.

11.2   COLOUR IN PAINTING

In this section, we will show more complex functions which colours perform in relation to visual objects on examples of artworks. To obtain a greater contrast, colours should be associated with objects having many common features, i.e. they should have similar forms. Painters, who care primarily for obtaining the strongest possible impact of colours, usually simplify forms and limit their diversity. Examples include impressionist paintings and some of Paul's Klee. In the picture made of squares only (Figure 11.15), the shapes of individual forms are the same, so we can say that all structures are created by colour. When we look at the picture without analyzing it, all structures interact with us, producing a total visual impression (sum of contrasts). If we like the image, it must have a sufficiently large number of hidden orders/structures. Let's indicate these structures using a numerical scheme (attached to Figure 11.15).

In general, it can be said that in this simple arrangement of squares, the colours were used to introduce as many separations/features/structures as possible. The more such qualitatively different separations are there the greater the total contrast and complexity (information content of the image). Let us follow how complexity is created in this picture, distinguishing structures from more general to specific ones.

FIGURE 11.15 Klee, *Table of Colour in Grey Major* (1930). A table with numbers facilitating the identification of individual squares (located in the image) was placed next to it. © Kunstmuseum Bern 2021.

1. Squares.
2. Three directions: vertical, horizontal (resulting from shapes) and diagonal (resulting from the ordering of colours).
3. Within the structure of the diagonal direction, different qualitative colour structures are distinguished, e.g. 28, 22, 16 (the same beige colour), 29, 23, 17 and 11 (alternately arranged two green and red squares).
4. Simple shapes, e.g. 21, 27 and 24, 30 (colour blue).

Contrasts:

1. The strongest contrast is the horizontal–vertical arrangement of directions in the image (resulting from shapes), with the diagonal location of the colour structures (ordering the colours along diagonal directions). Each square (shape of a square is their common feature) belongs to three orders (structures) along the following directions: horizontal, vertical and diagonal (differing features).
2. Separate diagonal structures (each square belongs to the diagonal structure and to the ordering inside this structure, thus creates a contrast).
    27 and 21 (the same blue colour).
    28, 22 and 16 (the same beige colour).
    29, 23, 17 and 11 (alternately arranged two green and red squares).
    30, 24, 18, 12 and 6 (symmetrical structure: two blue, white and two blue; square 6 is not blue but it has its function).
    25, 19, 13, 7 and 1 (two dark green, dark brown, white and dark green—more complicated structure).
    20, 14, 8 and 2 (green, from the lightest to the darkest).
    15, 9 and 3 (symmetry of brightness: green, blue—the brightest and grey).
    Similar structures can be seen along the second diagonal of the image, which will not be specified here.
3. The row of squares 11, 12, 13, 14 and 15 combines two structures: (1) the structure of larger squares (the top three rows) and (2) the brighter squares (the bottom four rows).
    A great contrast arises here, because the size and brightness are completely different, incomparable qualities, which in this picture are very strongly compared.
4. In addition to these structures, you can extract a few simple shapes, created by colours 21, 27 and 24, 30 (blue).
    6, 1 and 2 (dark colour).
    17, 23, 29 and 13, 19, 25 (dark colour).
    7, 12 and 9, 14 (light colour).

An important function of colour is also combining different objects in structures/wholes, thanks to which they gain new common features, which increases the contrast. In Cézanne's self-portrait (Figure 11.16), the cap, hair, beard and coat have a similar colour. Thanks to the binding, the contrast (of meanings and forms) of these objects increases.

FIGURE 11.16   Cézanne, *Self-portrait in a Casquette* (oil on canvas, 53 × 38 cm, 1875).
© The State Hermitage Museum, St. Petersburg 2021.

Colour can also be used to separate objects/forms in the image that are strongly related. In Matisse's painting (Figure 11.17), the strongly connected symmetrical parts of the face are partially separated by complementary colours: blue and yellow. Thanks to this, symmetrical facial half-shells gained new, strong differing features with a slight weakening of common features, which increased tension and contrast.

While in Impressionism, colour was largely autonomous, in post-Impressionism, colour still had a very important function, but already in combination with a compact, definitely defined form. Cézanne's painting is particularly important and revealing during this period, where the beginnings of Cubism and abstract art are already visible. All Cézanne's discoveries result from a careful and creative observation of nature. While maintaining the achievements of Impressionism, he additionally strengthened the visual structures by organizing the space, which influenced the stronger bonding of structures in his paintings, increasing their contrasts. Let us trace the contrasts in several of Cézanne's paintings in which colour, form and meaning are involved.

FIGURE 11.17 Matisse, *Portrait of Lydia Delectorskaya* (oil on canvas, 64.3 × 49.7 cm, 1947). © The State Hermitage Museum, St. Petersburg 2021.

In a still life with fruits (Figure 11.18), the more important contrasts are:

1. All elements running towards the centre of the perspective (these directions have been marked with lines), which is their common feature, create contrasts with each other.
2. Two groups of fruits form the forms of triangles (common feature), while in the left group, apples are separated, in the right one, they are not (different feature).
3. Apples 1, 2 and 3 and three small red spots on the vessel also create a contrast. Common features are the number of spots, shape, layout and colour; features that differ: size and meaning.
4. The shadow on the vessel on the right side creates a contrast with the painted pattern placed on the left side of this vessel. They have similar forms, but different meanings.

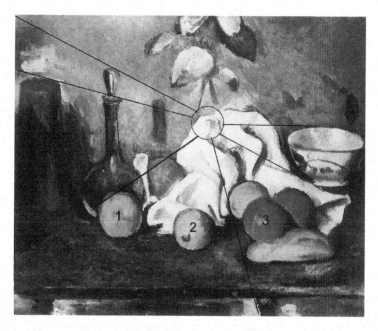

FIGURE 11.18   Cézanne, *Fruits* (oil on canvas, 45 × 54 cm, 1880). Guiding lines and apples' numbers have been added for interpretation purposes. © The State Hermitage Museum, St. Petersburg 2021.

In the portrait of *Smoker* (Figure 11.19), what is most interesting is the contrast of forms 1 and 3 (indicated in the diagram). A strong common feature of these forms is that both are created by the outline of the image and the similar places of the

FIGURE 11.19   Cézanne, *Smoker* (oil on canvas, 91 × 72 cm, 1892). A diagram explaining the image construction was placed next to it. © The State Hermitage Museum, St. Petersburg 2021.

FIGURE 11.20   Cézanne, *Still Life with a Curtain* (oil on canvas, 55 × 74.5 cm, 1895). The image contains elements necessary to explain its structure. © The State Hermitage Museum, St. Petersburg 2021.

almost symmetrical form 2. This creates a strong suggestion that forms 1 and 3 should be the same. Meanwhile, form 1 is almost a rectangle, and form 3 is a triangle. Connecting these forms with the same warm colour results in an even stronger impact of their shapes difference. Another important structure here is the simple form 2 (separated by a dark shade of green blue), binding the forms and meanings of man and the background, which are its elements.

The most important structures in Figure 11.20 are the structure of red colour, which creates the form of a parallelogram. Its elements are red apples and the pattern on the jug, differing in forms and meanings. An additional reinforcement of this contrast is the same arrangement and size of three red spots on the jug and three fruits below, constituting the opposite parallelogram angles. Other angles, in turn, form, similar in number and arrangement, groups of fruits. In these groups, there are five fruits, which is similar to the arrangement of five white spots marked with blue circles. Other structures are quadrilateral spots patterns marked with black and green lines.

12 Emergence as Contrast

12.1 EXISTING VIEWS

The word "emergence" comes from the Latin term "emergo, emergere", which means: "I am emerging" or "I arise". Intuitively emergence means the emergence of qualitatively new properties, forms and behaviours from the interaction between simpler elements. The given system property, "emergent", exists at the higher system level of the organization in relation to intra-system properties and processes that constitute the "emergence base". The colloquial description of this phenomenon is expressed by the statement that "the whole is more than the sum of its parts". The phenomenon is emergent, if it cannot be expressed, describing only its components. Even the most complete knowledge about the elements of a given system is insufficient to predict properties characteristic of the whole object. In the opinion of contemporary emergent theorist Philip Clayton (Clayton 2008), Aristotle and Plotinus were the precursors of emergentism. The announcement of this idea would be Aristotle's terms such as entelechia and formal causality, while in the case of Plotinus—a hierarchical concept of being. For later creators who have influence on the development of emergentism in the 20th century, Clayton includes Georg Wilhelm Hegel (metaphysics of becoming), Henri Bergson (creative evolution) and Alfred North Whitehead (process philosophy).

The origins of the concept of emergence should be traced to J.S. Mill in the mid-19th century. This author, in the work *The System of Logic* (Mill 1872), distinguishes the homopathic effect from the heteropathic effect. Both effects entail appropriate laws. Mill claims that the phenomena resulting from the action of homopathic laws are the mechanical consequences of the forces acting in them and do not go beyond the domain to which they belong (e.g. the physical world). In contrast, phenomena governed by heteropathic laws are not the result of purely mechanical action and belong to a higher domain than the one from which their causes originate. These phenomena based on heteropathic laws and effects, being rooted in a specific field of reality, go beyond it and form the basis for the formulation of a new, higher domain. It was only after 30 years that the term emergence was used (for the first time) by G.H. Lewes in his work *The Problems of Life and Mind* (Lewes 1875). It refers directly to the distinction of Mill, calling the heteropathic effect emergent and the homopathic effect resultant effect. In his work he writes:

> Every resultant is either a sum or a difference of the co-operant forces; their sum, when their directions are the same—their difference, when their directions are contrary. Further, every resultant is clearly traceable in its components, because these are homogeneous and commensurable. It is otherwise with emergents, when,

instead of adding measurable motion to measurable motion, or things of one kind to other individuals of their kind, there is a co-operation of things of unlike kinds. The emergent is unlike its components insofar as these are incommensurable, and it cannot be reduced to their sum or their difference.

An important stage in the history of the concept is the so-called British Emergence, which appeared in the 1920s. The result of the British Emergentist's work is the vision of reality with the hierarchical structure of beings that belong to the subsequent, dependent on each other's ontological levels. The way of their connection is determined by the relation of emergence—each subsequent level of the being hierarchy emerges from the previous one, which constitutes its "material" base. In turn what is "spiritual" on a given level is an emergent quality. This direction, however, lasted only for a short time (five years) and there were no creative followers. Successful examples of reductions in natural sciences (explanation of chemical processes based on knowledge about atoms construction and the discovery of the DNA structure, giving a chemical interpretation of the laws of genetics) weakened its attractiveness. Additionally, in the 1950s, emergentism was criticized by theoreticians of methodology of scientific research related to the so-called analytical philosophy of science, such as Carl Gustav Hempel, Paul Oppenheim and Ernest Nagel. After the collapse of the reductionist programme in the late 1960s, emergentism began to return to favour and is now a fairly common tool for the interpretation of properties autonomously of objects or complex systems, whose properties cannot be reduced to their so-called microstructures (the parts from which they are built, their properties and mutual relations—spatial or causal). At the same time, there is a discussion on the proper definition of this position. Those who stand on the ontological emergent position recognize that we cannot reduce the emergent property to the microstructure of the object, because the constitution of a complex whole introduces into the objectively existing reality some novelty (e.g. new quality or new causal forces). The opposite position is epistemological emergentism, recognizing that the mentioned impossibility is related only to human cognitive limitations, and what is considered emergent today, after improving scientific theories, may become a reducible property.

The following types of emergence are distinguished:

1. *Strong (ontological)*: relation describing the emergence of a qualitatively new level of existence from a more basic level; the most common are the two examples:
   - The phenomenon of consciousness.
   - Selected processes of quantum mechanics.
2. *Weak (epistemological)*: a relationship that relies on the subjective perception of emerging levels, while the fundamental level (usually physical) remains unchanged; examples are:
   - Cognitive processes.
   - Operating systems.
   - Biological evolution.

The following conditions of occurrence of ontological emergence are also mentioned (Kim 2006):

1. *Supervenience*: the property M supervises the properties of N_1, ..., N_n then and only if anything that has properties N_1, ..., N_n, it also necessarily has property M.
2. *Non-reducibility*: the M property is not reducible to the N_1, ..., N_n properties, if and only if property M cannot be derived, even in theory, from the most complete knowledge about the properties of N_1, ..., N_n.
3. *Downward/top-down causation*: properties from a higher H-level cause top-down properties from lower L if and only if: (1) L-level properties are possible to describe in terms that apply to property from level H; (2) L-level laws are separate from those at H-level; and (3) properties and laws from H-level must be included in the translation of properties from level L.

12.2   MODEL OF EMERGENCE

The concept of emergence (as it is defined) is intuitively associated with intense development and complexity, that is, something very valuable, which explains why it focuses attention and why we want to understand it better. The phenomenon of emergence is, on the one hand, the subject of research in particular sciences, where specific phenomena of emergence are examined and, on the other hand, subjected to formal analysis (mainly by the philosophy of mind), which on the basis of detailed knowledge tries to capture the meaning of the concept of emergence and formulate its definition. This analysis, however, is more concerned with the cognition of this phenomenon than the phenomenon itself. These approaches, which I would describe as empirical and epistemological, do not explain the objective causes of the phenomenon of emergence or its essence. We will try to discuss these reasons in the light of our considerations.

Let's look at the following definition of emergence:

> Property is emergent if it is a novel property of a system or an entity that arises when that system or entity has reached a certain level of complexity and that, even though it exists only insofar as the system or entity exists, it is distinct from the properties of the parts of the system from which it emerges.

(www.iep.utm.edu/emergenc/)

From our considerations (Chapter 10: "Interpretation of Basic Gestalt Concepts"), it follows that the elements connected together have more common features than when they occur separately. This statement can be understood tautologically, because the common features are connections; we will see, however, that the introduction of common features is crucial here. These additional (common) features just make the whole into something else or something more, than the sum of its parts. In Figure 12.1a, which shows the *general model of emergence*, we see a disordered set of squares. In Figure 12.1b, we have an intermediate state (part of the squares

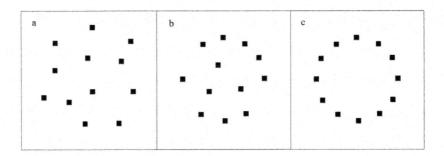

FIGURE 12.1 Model of emergence, a—unordered set of elements, b—intermediate state and c—maximum emergence.

formed a circle), and in Figure 12.1c, squares formed a circle (maximum emergence). Squares that found themselves in the structure of the circle gained new (common) features related to their location: the same distance from the centre of the circle and a similar distance from neighbouring elements.

The above model, although very simple, takes into account all aspects of the emergence definition cited above.

1. The formation of a new whole/quality—a circle.
2. The new whole (circle) is more complex in relation to the previous system. The greater complexity here results from having more (significant) common features by the constituent components (thanks to which their differing features also have a stronger impact). According to our previous considerations, the contrast and complexity are greater in this case.
3. The existence of a new quality (circle) depends on the existence of the system/whole that owns it.
4. The new quality does not have components from which the whole was created.

Emergence understood as above (as the creation of something more than the sum of its parts) is a special case of contrast/complexity. Recall that the contrast is also combining elements into a new structure/whole. While contrast is a general concept encompassing all kinds of both mental and physical interactions, the notion of emergence concerns only those contrasts, where contrasting elements form strongly distinctive wholes. Many such examples of emergent contrasts are analyzed in the Chapter 9, "Examples of Contrasts in Artworks" (Figures 9.1, 9.4, 9.9, 9.14, 9.15, 9.16, 9.17, 9.18, 9.22, 9.23, 9.26, 9.27 and 9.31). Because the principle of contrast can serve as a tool for analysis at every level of generality, let's analyze the general concept of emergence in a similar way to the above analyses of specific examples. Emergence creates a complex contrast in which the following contrasts add up:

1. Weak contrast is created by the collection of distinctive elements. Common features: similarity of elements. Features that differ: different position of elements (as example, we use here the features of elements from the emergence model).
2. Strong contrast is the whole/structure created from these elements thanks to their connection (common features). Common features: similarity of elements and similarity of the elements' positions to other elements. Features that differ: different position of elements on the plane.
3. Contrast between contrasts 1 and 2. Common features: the same elements. Features that differ: different layout, the emergence of a new quality in contrast 2 and different strengths of contrasts.
4. Contrast between contrast 3 and other contrasts (regarding other objects) from the observer's memory. Common features: effect of these contrasts in general. Features that differ: the nature of the effects (contrast currently perceived and contrast in the memory), strength and type of individual contrasts.

Although all the above-mentioned contrasts characterize the notion of emergence, contrasts 3 and 4 are the most important and distinctive for this concept. Contrast 3 even more strongly isolates the new quality (created by contrast 2), by combining it with the lack of such new quality in a similar set of elements (contrast 1). Contrast 4, on the other hand, verifies to what extent this new quality only applies to a given context and to what extent it is general. The above analysis on this general (abstract) level applies to all types of emergences (including strong, ontological and weak epistemological). It takes into account both the object and the subject of the analysis (which undoubtedly participates in the phenomenon of emergence) and also lists the basic impacts—contrasts taking part in the process of perceiving emergences. Thanks to this analysis, in conjunction with the visual model, one can understand the essence of the concept of emergence without engaging an extensive conceptual apparatus with which we are dealing in existing analyses. The analysis also answers the question about the metaphysical aspect of emergence, which the philosophy of mind is trying to answer today:

> The metaphysically interesting aspect of emergence is the question of what it takes for there to be genuinely distinct things. In other words, the question is whether a plausible metaphysical distinction can be made between things that are "nothing over and above" what constitutes them and those things that are "something over and above" their constituent parts. The notion of strong emergence that is predominant in philosophy is meant to capture this ontological distinction that was part of the initial motivation of the British emergentists and which is lacking in discussions of weak emergence.
>
> **(www.iep.utm.edu/emergenc/)**

Above we noticed that what separates (objects) from the environment are the common features of their components/elements (which are at the same time features that differentiate these components from the environment). The more strongly these features interact (they are stronger, or there are more of them), the stronger the integration of elements, i.e. the more coherent and distinctive the whole. (We treat both common and differentiating features as metaphysical concepts directly related to being and independent of our minds.) Objects specified in the question as "things that are nothing over and above what constitutes them" are poorly linked/integrated objects such as sets, collections and clusters of elements, which do not form coherent structures, and therefore their impact (contrast) is weak, so it also has a small complexity. Whereas "things that are something over and above their constituent parts", on the contrary, they are organized systems, coherent structures and wholes, which create large contrasts and therefore also have high complexity. The transition between these two types of distinguishing objects may be continuous (as shown in the above model); therefore the emergence may be graded and theoretically take values from close to 0 (weak isolation) to close to 100% (i.e. distinguish themselves very clearly). Distinguishing emergent wholes may be more connected with our mind (which is referred to as epistemological emergence) or with physical objects (ontological emergence). These proportions are different for each case and difficult to determine, which additionally hampers the bluntness of the very notion of emergence. Hence, there are also difficulties with their classification.

The above analysis of emergence confirms the universality of the definition of contrast as a tool for analysis at various levels of complexity and generality. It also confirms the integrative role of this definition. Thanks to it, we better understand the relationship of emergence with such concepts as contrast, complexity, development and value.

REFERENCES

Clayton, Ph. 2008. *Conceptual Foundations of Emergence Theory*. In Clayton, Ph. & Davies, P.C.W. (red.), *The Re-Emergence of Emergence: The Emergentist Hypothesis from Science to Religion*. Oxford: Oxford University Press, 5–6.

Kim, J. 2006. Emergence: core ideas and issues. *Synthese* 151: 547–559.

Lewes, G.H. 1875. *The Problems of Life and Mind*. London: Kegan Paul, Trench, Turber, & Co.

Mill, J. 1872. *The System of Logic*. London: Longmans, Greek, Leader, and Dyer.

13 Contrast and Subjectivity

What specifically affects us, for example, in a painting, or what we like, or what creates a contrast and how strong it is, depends also on the observer, and hence his/her knowledge, personality, taste, interests, attitude etc.—in short, on the attributes of the observer's mind. The latter includes the common and differentiating features as defined in reference to the perceived object, which also determines the observer's preferences. Besides universally preferred objects, there are also some (for example, in arts) that are not everybody's preference. This is where the notion that aesthetic judgements are subjective comes from. Let us examine this notion more closely. Assume that an observer is looking at a painting. First, the painting is reproduced by way of photons on the retina. Next, electric impulses transmit it to the brain, where it becomes connected with its structure. The measure of the observer's development is the number of new (differentiating) features that are added. How many differentiating features are added depends on how strongly they are attracted by common features, that is, on the number/strength of features common to the observer's mind and the observed object. The greater the number/power, the more numerous/stronger are the differentiating features that can be joined together. The following situations may arise in the perception process:

1. The perceived structure has no differentiating features that can enrich the observer's imagination (i.e. the structure is already familiar to the observer); therefore, it is not capable of arousing his/her interest.
2. The perceived structure has no or too few common features. No differentiating features can be connected, and there is no contrast or sense of development. The object is incomprehensible and uninteresting to the observer.
3. The perceived structure has more differentiating features that the observer is able to join together. If their number exceeds the observer's capabilities only slightly, this may arouse interest (appear mysterious) and offer potential for the observer's development. If they are too numerous, the structure may appear incomprehensible.
4. The perceived structure has some differentiating features, and common features are sufficiently numerous (but not excessively so) for them to be connected. This is the optimal situation: by making use of his/her own abilities, the observer can connect all the differentiating features of the object. The sense of development is maximized here (for a given observer), and perceiving the object produces strong aesthetic experiences.

To summarize, we have analyzed contrast in the subject–object relationship and, more precisely, the contrast between the structures of the perceived object and the structure of the observer's mind (understood as above). Just as in the case of contrast between two objects, the magnitude of contrast depends on the number/strength of common and differentiating features of contrasting structures. (Ignored here are the indirect contrasts, that is, those between the object and light and light and receptors, as well as contrasts within mental structures.)

The understanding of perception proposed here provides a resolution for the disputed issues regarding the objectivity and subjectivity of aesthetic experience, such as whether beauty is the product of the observer's mind or rather a special quality independent of the observer, by demonstrating that beauty is grounded in the subject and the object in equal measure; namely, it is founded on the relationship (contrast) between them.

14 Contrast as Cognition

14.1 ANALYSIS OF COGNITIVE PROCESS

Before we start our considerations, let's get acquainted with the current definition of the cognition:

> Cognition is the mental action or process of acquiring knowledge and understanding through thought, experience, and the senses. It encompasses many aspects of intellectual functions and processes such as attention, the formation of knowledge, memory and working memory, judgment and evaluation, reasoning and "computation", problem solving and decision making, comprehension and production of language. Cognitive processes use existing knowledge and generate new knowledge. The processes are analysed from different perspectives within different contexts, notably in the fields of linguistics, anesthesia, neuroscience, psychiatry, psychology, education, philosophy, anthropology, biology, systemics, logic, and computer science. These and other different approaches to the analysis of cognition are synthesised in the developing field of cognitive science, a progressively autonomous academic discipline.
> **(https://en.wikipedia.org/wiki/Cognition)**

In our considerations, we will focus on the general (abstract) aspect of the cognitive process and its essence. The object of cognition and the subject (mind) participate in the cognitive process. The object and the subject have common and different features, thus they create a contrast. Cognition consists of attaching (through common features) characteristics that distinguish the object (from the subject) by the subject. In this way, through contrast, the subject develops. By the subject of cognition, we mean any abstract or material object that has common and differentiating features with the subject and thus creates a contrast with it. Since we have already learned examples of contrasts of abstract objects, it is worth to consider a contrast of material objects as well. One example of such a contrast is the visual perception process directly related to cognition. The process proceeds as follows: *under the influence of light in the retina of the eye, electrical potentials are released, which as impulses are transmitted by visual path to the occipital part of the cerebral cortex, where they are converted into impressions conscious and interpreted, differentiated in terms of meaning.*

During the reception of light stimuli through the retina receptors, there is a contrast: light receptors. In order for contrast to occur, the interacting photons and atoms of the receptors must have sufficiently strong common features. These common features are: (1) contact in space and (2) identical energy of the photon and the energy level difference between the excited state and the ground state of the valence electron in the receptor atom. This allows the absorption of the photon and sends an electrical impulse to the brain. Electromagnetic waves of a different length (and therefore different energy) that fall on the retina do not react with it (they do not create a contrast) because these energy quanta are different. This example shows that both contrast and cognition can occur when the common features are strong enough. The process of cognition in the abstract sense is shown in Figure 14.1. The structures S1 and S2 are connected by means of common features (common part of the squares). These may be attributes attached during the perception that initiate the process of cognition. The layers of distinctive features that can be sequentially connected in the cognitive process have also been marked.

Assuming that S1 is a subject that joins differentiating features of the object S2, they will be the following features: brightness, size and direction. These attached features/structures are now common features of the subject and object. They can be treated as features of a concept or phenomenon as well as features of a real object.

The object–phenomenon–subject relation will be discussed in more detail in Section 20.3, "Physical and Conceptual Analysis".

Figure 14.1 also explains two issues: (1) how are the differing features attached? and (2) what connects different features within the object?

Features that differ in successive layers starting from the layer of common features are composed of two features: a common feature with the previous layer and a differing feature. Thanks to this, differentiating features can be attached. This

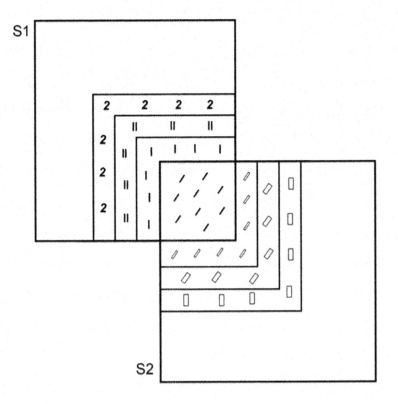

FIGURE 14.1 Subject–object connection (contrast).

complexity of features also allows combining various features within the whole of the object.

At this point one may ask what then combines these two different features within one (complex) feature, just like we asked what connects the various (complex) features within the object? The answer will be the same, that is, we will again treat the features included in the complex feature as complex. Proceeding so on, we come to the basic feature, which must also be composed of two features, but no longer divisible. Let us assume that such a primary (simplest) feature and at the same time the basic component of reality is a feature consisting of zero and one. These two features are related to each other (they are in a sense the whole) by the logical dependence that neither one nor zero can be distinguished independently (without the presence of a second characteristic). In Figure 14.1, visual characteristics such as size, direction and brightness combine into composite features by overlapping. Similarly (by imposition), one can also understand the combination of zero and one (as will be discussed in Chapter 17, "Contrast as Being", and Chapter 20, "Binary Model of Universe".

Many current theories in cognitive science concerning organization of knowledge are based on the assumption that concepts consist of different types of information. However, there are many discrepancies as to how different kinds of knowledge about the same object are integrated (the "binding problem"). The above understanding of the complexity of object features contributes to this problem an explanation. Now, our conception will be used for a more detailed interpretation of key issues related to the cognitive process.

14.2   INTERPRETATIONS OF COGNITIVE CONCEPTS

14.2.1   COGNITION

Cognition refers to a person's ability to have knowledge of and learn about reality. From a psychological perspective, this concept can be defined as the body's ability to receive information from the environment, process it and use it to manage its own or someone else's behaviour.

Interpretation:

Receiving information from the environment is the attachment of objects features by the subject through their common features. Information processing consists in organizing or linking various features within the mind through their common features in the structures of these features. The use of processed information (formed structure of features) to control own or someone else's behaviour relies on the similarity of structures in the mind and structures of reality in which the subject participates (is bound by common features).

Mental models: cognitive psychology and cognitive approach postulate that the knowledge of reality does not create the mind through passive summation of data received from sense organs and their storage, but in an active way, as a kind of model, mapping or representing real objects in some symbolic form of cognitive structures.

Interpretation:

The creation of the model of reality by the mind consists in attaching the features of the object by the subject and combining them (thanks to common features) into coherent structures-models.

Cognitive processes: Cognitive processes, and in a broader sense, the cognitive system (mind), are not exclusively a human domain; they are rather a property of the nervous system, the same as the ability to cause muscle cramps and the movement of animals.

Interpretation:

We can talk about cognitive processes when, at the time of connecting structures, at least one of them is a cognizing subject. Cognitive processes can be generalized for joining by any structure (treated as a subject) of other structures (similar to the example above).

14.2.2   PERCEPTION

Perception: this is responsible for receiving information from the environment. It is associated with separate sensory modalities, and then we talk about visual, auditory, taste, olfactory and tactile perception.

Interpretation:

Perception is the attachment of object features by the subject (i.e. through common features of the object and the senses of the subject).

Sensory reception: early process of passive registration of information, reflection of stimuli in receptors (Nęcka et al. 2006), which is identified with the first stages of information processing of a given sensory modality in the nervous system.

Interpretation:

Reflecting stimuli in receptors is a connection of stimulus and receptor through their common features; e.g. in visual perception these commonalities are (as we have already discussed) photon energy and energy needed to change the orbit of the electron in the receptor's atom.

Perception: a later, active process, involving the interpretation of sensory data using contextual guidelines, attitudes and previously acquired knowledge (Nęcka et al. 2006). The process of perception leads to the creation of an impression-image that was created on the basis of the provided stimuli.

Interpretation:

Let's try to consider how the image is created. The process of perception that leads to the appearance of an image is a combination of the stimulus structure (and indirectly the object) with the structure of our mind (thanks to the common features). The image is created due to the high complexity (contrast) of these structures. Where does this complexity come from? Important here is the considerable complexity of the structures themselves (as components) and their contrast, or the strong bonding of their differing features.

We know that the structure of the visual stimulus is the most complex of all the structures of sensory stimuli. However, the structure contained in mind is the features/components of stimuli recalled from memory and, above all, the structure of space, which on the path of evolution was permanently formed in the part of the brain related to the sense of sight. Its complexity results from the compression of information contained in the spatial dimension (space as the compression of information will be discussed in Chapter 20, "Binary Model of Universe"). This a priori structure of space overlaps with all visual stimuli (of the outside world), combining them (organizing) into objects. Overlapping as we know is a very strong common feature. Thus, a strong contrast is created, which identifies with the image. We owe understanding of space and time as a priori imagination to Immanuel Kant (Kant 1952). While space and time were previously regarded as empirical impressions, he noticed that any external experience already implies the imagination of space ("because where there is no space there can be no question of something external"). In order for us to be able to project impressions outside, we must already have the impression of space. Kant's argument is illustrated by the following excerpt:

> What is space and time, whose imaginations are non-empirical and necessary? They are nothing real, because then the natural way to know them would be an empirical way, and their imaginations would not have the feature of necessity. After all, how can space and time be real like things? It is hard to even imagine: there would be some vessels containing all objects, but vessels of a special kind, because they were infinite and without walls. If they are not real, they must be ideal; they do not belong to the world of things, they come from our senses. Our senses do not produce their impressions, but they add them to them. Receiving impressions, they capture them in a certain order, either as simultaneous or as successive ones. The first order is called space, the second time.
>
> **(Tatarkiewicz 1981)**

The above explanation is an example of a wider change that Kant made in the relationship between the object and the subject. It turned out that the subject is not a contradiction of the object, as previously thought, but a condition of the object. The traditional contradiction of experience and a priori thought turned out to be defective, because thought is not the opposite, but an essential component of experience.

14.2.3 ATTENTION

Attention is responsible for selecting information. It is inseparable from the processes of perception to the extent that in some situations it is convenient to treat attention as if it were a perceptual process.

Interpretation:
Attention (focused on a given object) is the largest perceptual contrast at the moment in relation to other currently perceived contrasts.

Bottom-up attention: this is triggered by the environment and an example may be an orientational reflex. Orientation reflex is a mechanism of attention, the function of which is to open the cognitive system for change or a new stimulus. It consists in directing the receptors to the source of stimulation, which is accompanied by motor activity, facilitating its reception.

Interpretation:

Bottom-up attention appears as a result of an external stimulus that is strong enough (it has strong enough common features with the subject) that it creates a greater contrast with it than the structures in mind, the attachment of which was expected next.

Top-down attention: it is triggered by the body; it involves the taking of a purposeful, volitional activity.

Interpretation:

Top-down attention appears as a result of the contrast in the mind that is stronger than the others, but it is consistent with the expectation.

Selective attention: this refers to the selection of information available in the environment, the ability to focus on one selected aspect of the environment, i.e. direct the attention channel to the selection of specific information. Sometimes this is described by the term of directing the field of attention or focusing attention on the stimulus. Selectivity of attention not only concerns perception, but also complex cognitive processes. Not only sensory data, but also thinking operations are selected.

Interpretation:

Because attention must be subject to constant changes (just like the whole reality), therefore focusing on one object is in fact a constant shift of attention to something else, returning to a given object. Selectivity of attention consists in choosing the information that creates the greatest contrast with the current state of mind (related to an object or problem).

Sustained attention: this concerns the ability to maintain attention (in the sense of selective attention) for a long time on the same aspect of the environment.

Interpretation:

This ability results from the relatively stronger common features (integration) of the structure of the mind with a given aspect of the environment than with others.

Divided attention: this concerns the possibility of directing attention (in the sense of selective attention) to two aspects of the environment at the same time, selecting information with two channels of information processing at the same time (the nervous system processes information in a parallel manner, but this issue is not identical with the divisibility of attention).

Interpretation:

The division of attention occurs when the attention is quickly transferred from one structure/object of environment to the other and back to the first, so that we have the feeling of simultaneous perception of these objects. It involves increasing the integration of their structures in the mind. Switching the attention from one environment object to the other is due to the fact that both objects interact with a similar force, larger than the other surrounding objects.

Alternating attention: this refers to the ability to switch attention (in the sense of selective attention) between two aspects of the environment from one to the other, directing the attention channel (or focusing attention) once on one and once on the other. It is assumed here that the divisibility of attention consisting in the actual selection by more than one attention channel is not possible. This issue also includes a special situation, when the attention must be switched from one aspect of the environment to another and then again to the former, which can alternatively explain the issues of divisibility of attention.

Interpretation:

The mind joins/perceives the structures of the environment in order. After connecting one, connect the next one. The first in order are those structures that have more features in common with the current state of mind (it can be explained as follows: let's assume that we have some object 1 (having 100% of its features) and two other objects, object 2 having 99% of the features of object 1 and object 3 having 98% of the features of object 1. In abstract terms, we can say that object 2 is more connected to object 1 than object 3. So how to understand the sequence of these connections? It seems rational to identify tautologically the sequence with the number of common features, because there are no other factors determining the sequence). There are three possibilities: (1) if each subsequent one is different, then it involves learning more and more area; (2) if every second subsequent one is different, then we deal with selectivity of attention, that is, continuous repetition of focus on the same aspect; (3) if every second subsequent one is the same, then we deal with alternating attention, that is, the repetition of switching attention from one object to another and vice versa. What is the difference between alternating attention and the divided attention? In the alternating attention, we do not have the feeling of simultaneous perception of two objects, which may be related to the extended time of their perception.

Vigilance: this refers to waiting for the appearance of specific information and ignoring other information. The data that the subject expects can be called a signal and the data ignored as noise.

Interpretation:

Waiting for the appearance of specific information is tantamount to having an idea of this information and therefore a part of the features of this information. While waiting for the information, we compare its image with subsequent information being attached, each time returning to the image. Vigilance is similar then to selectivity of attention, where every second subsequent information is different. The appearance of the expected information is tantamount to a high contrast of this information with the image, much larger than with the other, ignored information.

Search: this concerns the active search for specific information among a set of various information, the ability to deliberately and actively select specific data from the environment. As in the case of vigilance, the expected and wanted data can be defined as a signal, however, the remaining, ignored data are referred to as distractors, i.e. information that interferes with or makes it difficult to find a signal.

Interpretation:

The search is similar to vigilance with the difference that it is active while vigilance is passive. What is the difference between the passivity of waiting and the activity of search? Passivity is when the information reaches us, we only need to recognize it. In the case of searching, in addition to recognizing information, it is necessary to perform activities related to their location and determining the method of searching.

14.2.4 MEMORY

Memory is the ability to store information and consists of various systems and different processes. There are two main memory systems.

Interpretation:

What we call memory or information stored in memory can be identified with information, features and structures that change slowly (slowly disintegrate) in the mind (hence the association with storage).

Declarative/explicit memory: this is a memory system in which stored information is easy to be understood, easy to verbalize or visualize. From a neurobiological perspective, this memory system is associated with the functioning of the hippocampus—a structure located in the medial part of the temporal lobe of the brain.

Interpretation:

Information that is easy to be aware of are the ones among those remembered, that are the most influential (they create the highest contrast and are the most complex), which is why they are easier to pass into the consciousness.

Sensory memory: this is a more perceptual phenomenon than memory, associated with the registration of the stimulus of a given modality; sensory memory stores a small amount of information in a very short time.

Interpretation:

It can be said that sensory memory is the first stage of memorization. To the next stage, more permanent working memory will pass those stimuli, which will be more strongly associated with other structures of the mind, for example, by repeating a given stimulus or through a greater strength of its impact.

Working memory: the terminology depends on a specific theory; it concerns storing a small amount of verbal or non-verbal information that is currently used. Working memory is treated not only as a buffer storing information passively for a short period of time, but as a kind of working space in which conscious processing of information takes place. The theory of working memory connects memory processes with executive functions and attention.

Interpretation:

It can be said that working memory is the second stage of memorization (already more durable than sensory memory). At this stage, the information begins to be processed.

Long-term memory (LTM): this refers to information stored permanently, consolidated. This system also speaks of the so-called phases, processes or memory activities, such as saving or recognition.

Interpretation:

Recording information (encoding) involves repeating the exposure of a given stimulus and therefore multiple integration of the corresponding structure in the mind. An important consequence of the repetition is that with each subsequent integration, the structure integrates in a little different context (of other structures in mind), creating connections with this new context and thus increasing the number of connections with other structures of the mind; it consolidates it more and takes root in the structure of the mind. The more repetitions, the more persistent their record is.

Recognition: recognition or recognition memory is a process less aggravating to the cognitive system compared to free reminding, involving the identification of incoming information from sense organs as already known.

Interpretation:

Recognition memory is a contrast of incoming information with these memorized information that have the most in common with them.

Procedural memory: this includes skills learning and habit learning, gradual acquisition of practice in both cognitive and motor-control activities, interaction of the sense of balance and visual-motoric coordination, such as cycling.

Interpretation:

Procedural memory is undoubtedly a non-volatile memory; hence it can be presented as a long-term memory. Saving and memorizing information in this memory is associated with a large number of repetitions of the exposure of a given stimulus and therefore multiple integration of the corresponding structures in the mind.

14.2.5 THINKING

Thinking: usually, definitions of thinking are formulated in general, indicating the most characteristic feature of this type of processes. The feature is that thinking is aimed at creating a model of reality in order to perform various operations and transformations on this model and not on real reality. Here is an example of one of the definitions of thinking.

> Thinking is the process of combining the elements of the cognitive representation of the world in longer sequences, replacing real observable behaviour in the real physical or social world, freeing us from the immediate consequences of our actions—thinking is a substitute for action.
>
> **(Nęcka et al. 2006)**

This understanding of thinking comes from Kenneth James Williams Craik—one of the first to realize that machines share with the brain certain principles of functioning. In 1943, he published the book *The Nature of Explanation*, where he considered thought as a term for the conscious working of a highly complex machine, viewing the brain as a calculating machine which can model or parallel external events, a process that is the basic feature of thought and explanation.

Interpretation:
    The mind as the most complex structure of reality, thanks to thinking (information processing), can model any existing structures of reality by organizing its characteristics/information (analogous to reality) and also create (theoretically) any combination—organization of those features/information that reality does not have. This thinking/modelling has improved considerably and is still improving to a large extent, thanks to computers and computer simulations.

REFERENCES

Kant, I. 1952. *Kritik der urteilskraft* [Critique of Judgment]. Oxford: Clarendon Press.
Nęcka, E., Orzechowski, J. & Szymura, B. 2006. *Psychologia Poznawcza* [Cognitive Psychology]. Warszawa: PWN.
Tatarkiewicz, W. 1981. *Historia Filozofii* [*History of Philosophy*]. Warszawa: PWN, 2, 56.

15 Mind-Body Problem

15.1 EXISTING VIEWS

Currently, the main research related to the mind-body problem is focused on determining the nature of the mind and consciousness, and how the mental processes affect (if they affect) the functioning of the brain and vice versa. Two groups of views stand out here: dualism and monism. Dualists believe that the mind is independent of the body ontologically as an independent substance (substantial dualists), or is a group of independent properties that have emerged from the brain and cannot be reduced to it (property dualists). According to the monists, the mind and body are not ontologically different beings (independent substances).

Dualism: in Western philosophy, one of the earliest discussions about duality is found in Plato's writings, which maintained that human "intelligence" (being the ability of the mind or soul) cannot be identified with the body or explained in its terms. However, the most known version of duality comes from René Descartes (*Meditations on the First Philosophy*, 1641), who claimed that the mind is nonphysical and therefore, non-spatial substance ("res cogitans"). Descartes was the first to identify the mind with consciousness and self-awareness and to separate the concept of "mind" from the brain, which in turn recognized as the seat of intelligence. For this reason, it is often acknowledged that he formulated the mind-body problem in a form that functions to this day.

The most commonly used argument in favour of duality refers to the common sense of intuition that the conscious experience is different from inanimate matter. If you ask what the mind is, the average person would say that the mind is identical to "him/her", with their personality, soul or something else. The suggestion that "his/her" mind is simply a brain could be considered absurd and incomprehensible. Many contemporary mind philosophers believe that such intuitions are deceptive and that we should examine them critically, referring to empirical scientific knowledge, to determine whether they are justified (Hart 1996).

Another important argument for duality is that the mental and the physical seem to have different and irreconcilable properties (Jackson 1982). Mental events have a subjective quality, while physical events do not. Mind philosophers call the subjective aspects of mental events "qualia". Qualia are referred to as "how it is to feel pain", "how to see a specific shade of blue" (Nagel 1974), etc. Pain is felt "somehow". Frank Jackson argued in favour of the thesis that even with full knowledge of someone's brain, we still do not have access to the qualia of that person.

If consciousness (mind) can exist independently on physical reality (brain), it should be explained how they affect one another, in other words, how (immaterial) mind is "coupled" with the (material) body. Descartes suggested that the place where this occurs is the pineal gland. Another explanation was proposed, among others, by

Arnold Geulincx and Nicolas Malebranche. In their opinion, all interactions between the mind and the body require a direct intervention of God.

Another possible argument, advanced by Clive Staples Lewis (1947), is an argument of reason: if the monists are right and all our thoughts are the effects of physical causes, then we have no reason to assume that they are also the consequences of a rational background. Though knowledge is acquired through reasoning to consequences, if monism is correct, there should not be a way to learn this, or anything else—we should not even suppose that, unless by accident.

The argument of the logical possibility of the zombie existence is based on the thought experiment proposed by Todd Moody and developed by David Chalmers in his book *The Conscious Mind* (Chalmers 1996). The basic idea is that one can imagine the existence of a human body without any associated conscious states. Chalmers' argument is that it seems plausible that such a being could exist because all that is needed is that only the things that the physical sciences describe and observe about a human being must be true of the zombie. It is relatively easy to imagine, because none of these teachings refers to consciousness or other mental phenomena, and any physical phenomenon can (by definition) be described scientifically in the language of physics. Others, like Daniel C. Dennett, gave a counterargument that the concept of a philosophical zombie is incoherent or unlikely. Starting from the position of physicalism, he claims that either everyone believes that they are zombies or nobody thinks that he is a zombie, since the feeling of being or not being zombie results from physical phenomena occurring in human brains. Dennett writes: "Zombies think they are aware, they think they have qualia, they think they feel pain—they are simply wrong (according to this regrettable tradition) in a way that neither they nor we could ever discover" (Dennett 1995).

Monism: unlike dualists, monists do not acknowledge the existence of any fundamental metaphysical divisions—the world is uniform ontologically. The monistic character of reality has been present in some directions of Indian and Chinese philosophy for over 2,500 years. This view in the philosophy of the West appeared for the first time in the 5th century BC in the thought of Parmenides and was disseminated by a 17th-century philosopher—Baruch Spinoza. Currently, the most common form of monism in Western philosophy is physicalism. Physicalistic monism assumes that everything that exists is physical, where the word "physical" is understood in accordance with the current state of knowledge in physics. However, many different expressions of monism are possible. One of them is idealism, which assumes that the only mental substance exists. The extreme idealism represented by e.g. George Berkeley (subjective idealism) is rare in contemporary Western thought. There is, however, a related form of this position called panpsychism, according to which all things are partly psychological. Followers of this view were Alfred North Whitehead and David Ray Griffin. Phenomenalism is a theory that only representations (or sensory data) of external objects exist. This view was briefly accepted by Bertrand Russell and many logical positivists in the first half of the 20th century, such as Alfred Ayer. Another option is to accept the existence of a fundamental substance that is neither physical nor mental. Mental and physical could be the properties of this one neutral substance (neutral stuff). This position was adopted by Baruch Spinoza and popularized by Ernst Mach in the 19th century. This neutral monism, as it is usually called, can be treated as an intermediate between monism and dualism.

15.2 MIND-BODY PROBLEM (UNDERSTANDING ATTEMPT)

The above characteristics show that there is no consensus in understanding the mind-body relationship, and there is a wide variety of views. It also indicates the lack of convincing arguments/evidence confirming the validity of one of them. Let's try to take a stand on this dispute, using the concept of contrast. In Chapter 12, "Emergence as Contrast", we used the definition of contrast to analyze the concept of emergence. This analysis showed that the reason for emergence, i.e. the emergence of new, coherent wholes as a result of mutual interactions of their potential (future) components are additional common features that these components gain as soon as they are combined into the whole. Because this is a general explanation of the causes of emergence, it should also apply to specific cases of it, including consciousness, which is also considered a kind of emergence. To explain the reasons for the emergence of consciousness, we must define what its components are. Let's assume that these components are energy pulses (electrochemical). Our considerations show that if they gain a sufficient number of new common features, a new emergent whole will be created, which should be perceived as consciousness by a sufficiently high degree of isolation. New common features should be understood as additional relationships/ connections between impulses (or more precisely—impulses structures). Thanks to them, the new whole should stand out more strongly, like the circle in our emergence model (which is also a new quality emerging from the area of disordered visual elements). This explanation also creates the possibility of empirical verification, e.g. by checking how the number of neural connections (common features) affects the appearance of conscious states. Previous brain neurological studies show that such a relationship exists. This hypothesis is also supported by the fact that as the number of connections increases, the complexity of the impulse structure also increases.

Now let's consider another argument and think about how mental feelings arise, i.e. a feeling of understanding, realizing something, imagining something and feeling of pleasure. The feeling of understanding a new concept/term arises when we place them in a sufficient number of contexts, i.e. we associate with various existing structures in our mind, thus increasing the number of connections. These connections, which seem obvious, correspond to electrical neural connections. Similarly, one can explain the understanding of a problem, solving a task (e.g. mathematical), recognizing a musical piece or familiar face, or noticing hidden figures in Picasso's paintings. In all these cases, we are dealing with an increase in the number of combinations of various elements/components necessary to form a properly coherent, emerging (whole) entity.

On the other hand, isolation can be equated with impact and existence (what is not isolated cannot be seen). Interactions understood in this way can be equated with energy because we do not know any interactions that would not require energy. (The word "energy" comes from the Ancient Greek word *energeia* meaning action.) In fact, there is currently no more detailed definition. Physics defines energy as equivalent to work (to which it can be used), while work is the product of path and force (on which force acts), but force is again defined as action. So isolation (separation and standing out), interaction, energy and strength should be considered as synonymous, basic and undefinable. So if we extract consciousness, emotional states, sensory and mental feelings (qualia), it means that they exist. By saying something exists, we mean physical existence. Isolation/existence is not monovalent and can be graded (something can be more strongly or less separated). This is associated with the attribution to stronger degrees of extraction—physical properties and to weaker—mental properties. In addition to the power of isolation, we can talk about the complexity of extracting wholes, i.e. values (the definition of value as complexity was presented in Chapter 8, "Contrast as Value"). Although consciousness does not emerge as strongly as, e.g., a table or chair, it is undoubtedly of greater value.

Another more detailed argument in favour of materiality of the mind/consciousness is the fact that (logically speaking) there can be no structure (also in the mind) without elements that somehow (in it) separate. What is extracted, and thus somehow interacting, must have energy. In the case of the mind, it would be a specific form of energy (electrochemical impulses). So mental structures must also have energy. This is illustrated by the following example:

Consider the abstract binary structure in our mind: 100101101. Zeros and ones symbolize two different elements that must be present for the structure to exist. Suppose zero means no energy. If one also did not have energy, we would have only zeros. One may wonder at this point whether the condition of energy possession by abstract structures/sets (in the mind) is related to the division into distributive sets concerning abstract objects and collective (mereological) ones regarding physical objects. A doubt arises whether if we consider the concepts as physical objects (in our mind), then the concept of distributive (abstract) sets loses sense and should be included in the concept of collective sets.

Consider the following example: two mereological sets consisting of a different number of elements can be the same set (e.g. a set of two hydrogen atoms and a set of four elementary particles making up these atoms: two protons and two electrons). However, if two distributive sets have a different number of elements, they are definitely different. The set of two hydrogen atoms is numerically different from the set of two protons and two electrons. It follows from the above that, despite assigning energy (in the mind) to elements of the set consisting of two hydrogen atoms, another set consisting of two protons and two electrons is also conceivable, to which another energy will be assigned (in the mind). Hence, the conclusion that the attribution of energy to abstract concepts does not affect the division under consideration. In other words, the energy of the concepts of physical objects (in our mind) is not correlated with the energy of real physical objects.

The above arguments speak for the unification of the mind and body, which are the closest to the concepts of physicalist monism saying that the only existing type of being are physical objects (just like the physical object is the circle from Figure 12.1). Our considerations also show that mental states are a form (type, structure) of energy, just like forms of energy are all other objects of reality that we perceive. It is also important that the unifying treatment of the mind as a physical object creates opportunities for mind research that increases the likelihood of understanding mental processes. The following text speaks of this (Duch 2000):

> Consciousness research has been taboo for a long time. The problem of the nature of consciousness was mainly discussed by philosophers speculating on the subject of the mind in total detachment from neuroscience. The exception here is created by Patricia Churchland *Neurophilosophy* (Churchland 1986) critical of functionalism, in particular arguments regarding the independence of psychological states from brain states. Unfortunately, few mind philosophers have gone in this direction and there is still a great deal of confusion in this area. On the one hand, some philosophers propose the rejection of all intermediate levels of description, claiming that there are only neurophysiological states and consciousness (Searle 1992), criticizing the study of brain processing information. This is an extremely destructive approach, because it is impossible to construct meaningful models of the mind without introducing a whole series of intermediate levels—neurobiological facts must be the basis, but without theoretical models and computer simulations that allow making and testing hypotheses regarding brain functioning, we will remain at the level of behaviourism. On the other hand, discussions about the mind are led astray by philosophical mathematicians, arguing— in isolation from both cognitive psychology and neuroscience—for the existence of "secret mental properties whose understanding will require a review of fundamental physical theories".
>
> **(Penrose and Gardner 1994)**

Our considerations regarding emergence and its visual model show that the surprise associated with the emergence of new wholes results from the gradual accumulation of changes (in a given area, e.g. the area of the mind, or a set of squares), which from a certain moment begin to form noticeable (isolated) orderings, as in the process of crystallization, an example of recognizing a Dalmatian in the speckle pattern, the appearance of a sense of understanding, regaining consciousness after waking up or emerging circle in the emergence model. By ordering, it is meant a known pattern, which, due to the fact that it is known, from a certain moment when it begins to be recognized, accelerates and strengthens emergence (because it imposes a known pattern on a still poorly isolated object). This acceleration (associated with what is referred to as the "explanatory gap") causes surprise and is difficult to trace/explain. Theoretically, however, this difficulty can be overcome, as it has already happened in many other cases of emergence.

15.3   QUALIA

The issue of qualia or our conscious and subjective experiences is directly related to the problem of mind-body and consciousness. Qualia are characterized as first-person mental states for which we have introspective access. They usually refer to some property of a given object and have a purely phenomenal, empirical character. Mental states that have qualia can be divided into sensory experiences (feeling of bitter taste, seeing blue colour and hearing the sound of a guitar), all kinds of bodily sensations (toothache, feeling of thirst and hunger) and emotions (shame, contentment and love).

Many philosophers, such as Galen Strawson (1994) believe that qualia also have mental states, such as propositional attitudes (belief in the correctness of their theses, sense of understanding a given sentence and desire to be understood by others), and conscious introspective experiences in the form meta-reflection (the feeling that I am thinking about what I write). The problem of qualia is difficult to explain for both philosophers of mind and cognitive scientists (Pawłowski 2009: 184):

> Many philosophers say that explaining how mental states are reduced to physical states will never be resolved. This position was one of the first to be formulated by Joseph Levine (1983), saying that there is a gap in the explanation between the mental state and the physical state. If we define heat as the movement of molecules, we can consider this definition sufficient. The problem will arise if we want to define pain as a neuron movement (C-fiber firing).

In the philosophical literature there are many thought experiments related to the subject of qualia: one of the most famous is the case of imprisoned Mary. This example was first formulated by Frank Jackson (1982). Like most such experiments, it tries to raise the problem of qualia reduction to physical states.

> Mary is a brilliant colour scientist who has spent her entire life in a black-and-white room. Although she has normal colour vision, her confinement has prevented her from ever having any colour sensations. While in the room, Mary has studied colour science through black and white textbooks, television, etc. And in that way she has learned the complete physical story about colour experience, including all the physical facts about the brain and its visual system. She knows all the physical facts about colour. But she has never seen anything in colour. Now suppose that Mary is one day released from her room and presented with a ripe tomato. What should we imagine happens? Most people have the very strong intuition that Mary learns something from this perceptual experience. "Aha!" she might say. "Now I finally know what the colour red is like".
>
>   The Mary case is the centerpiece of Jackson's knowledge argument against physicalism. While in the room, Mary knew all the physical facts about colour, including the colour red. When she is released from the room, Mary learns something about the colour red, namely, what seeing red is like. What Mary learns consists of new, factual information. So there are facts about colour in addition to all the physical facts about colour (since Mary already knew all the physical facts about colour). Thus, the argument goes, physicalism is false.
>
>   In the quarter century since Jackson's development of the knowledge argument, a vast literature has developed in response to it. Attempting to save physicalism, some philosophers deny that Mary learns anything at all when she leaves the room. If we really imagine that Mary has learned all the physical facts about colour while in the room, then there would be no "Aha!" moment when she is shown a ripe tomato. We are led to think otherwise only because we typically fall short of imagining what we've been asked to imagine—we imagine only that Mary knows an immense amount about colours, that she has mastered all the information contained in our present science of colour, which still remains incomplete.
>
>   To pursue strategy (2), the physicalist might argue that Mary doesn't gain any new knowledge when she leaves the room; rather, she simply comes to apprehend an old fact under a new guise. While in the room, she did not have the conceptual apparatus she

needed in order to apprehend certain colour facts in a phenomenal way. Having seen colour, she has now gained new concepts—phenomenal concepts—and thus is able to re-apprehend the same facts she already knew in a different way. Whether there are genuinely phenomenal concepts, and if so, whether they do the work in answering the knowledge argument that the physicalists want them to, has recently been generating a growing literature of its own.

(https://iep.utm.edu/qualia/)

Although the above logical arguments for physicalism are correct, they do not bring constructive knowledge and do not explain the problem. Let's try to strengthen this view by adding some new arguments here. While consciousness is considered the emergence of neuronal processes in our brain, qualia can be considered as emergent states of consciousness, i.e. the structures that are emerging (or more distinct). So it is like emergence of emergence. Therefore, although the rules are the same as for emergence of consciousness, qualia have got a separate name. The essence of emergence is the appearing qualitative leap in relation to gradually increasing changes in a given area, as a result of obtaining additional features by the potential components of the new whole (which was discussed earlier). The variety, intensity and incomparability of quality-qualia as well as the difficulty in understanding/ explaining them are due to the emergence of a new quality and the inability to trace too quickly the growing changes in this process. If we had the opportunity to trace the growth of changes in the brain during which we begin to see, e.g. red colour (similar to the formation of a circle in our emergence model), then its appearance would not surprise us as it is no longer a surprise that heat is the result of molecule movement. Qualia as emergent wholes are unique because they characterize our mind above all. However, similar examples are also found in physics, chemistry and biology, where we also observe large qualitative leaps.

- For example, in physics, elementary particles such as electrons and protons do not have colour. Only when combined into atoms can they absorb and emit specific wavelengths, which are described as having colour.
- Another example is the fact that radio and light waves are electromagnetic waves of different frequencies, as demonstrated by Heinrich Hertz (1881– 1884) and which was previously predicted by Maxwell's theory of James Clerk.
- In biology, one example of the emergence discovery was the statement (by biologists Matthias Jakob Schleiden and Theodor Schwann) that all plants and animals are made of cells.

If we think even more broadly, we will come to the conclusion that not only qualia and other emergent wholes are surprising to us, but also everything that in any way (in the mind and outside it) is isolated—and therefore exists (the identity of isolation and existence has already been discussed). So it's worth realizing that the question about the phenomenon of qualia is synonymous with the question about the phenomenon of existence.

REFERENCES

Chalmers, D. 1996. *The Conscious Mind*. New York: Oxford University Press.

Churchland, P.S. 1986. *Neurophilosophy. Toward a Unified Science of the Mind/Brain*. MIT Press, Bradford Book.

Dennett, Daniel C. 1995. The unimagined preposterousness of zombies. *Joural of Consciousness Studies* 2(4): 322–326.

Duch, W. 2000. *Świadomość i Dynamiczne Modele Działania Mózgu* [Consciousness and Dynamic Models of Brain activity]. Toruń: Uniwersytet Mikołaja Kopernika.

Hart, W.D. 1996. Dualism. In Guttenplan, Samuel (org.), *A Companion to the Philosophy of Mind*. Oxford: Blackwell, 265–267.

Jackson, F. 1982. Epiphenomenal qualia. *Philosophical Quarterly* 32: 127–136.

Levine, J. 1983. Materialism and qualia: the explanatory gap. *Pacific Philosophical Quarterly* 64: 354–361.

Lewis, C.S. 1947. *Miracles*. London: Collins/Fontana.

Nagel, T. 1974. What is it like to be a bat? *The Philosophical Review* 83(4): 435–450.

Pawłowski, M. 2009. *Czy Qualia są Granicą tego co Możemy Poznać? Problem Luki w Wyjaśnianiu* [Are Qualia the Limit of What We Can Know? The Problem of Explanation Gap]. Szczecin: Pomorski Uniwersytet Medyczny, 184.

Penrose, R. & Gardner, M. 1994. *The Emperor's New Mind: Concerning Computers, Minds and the Laws of Physics*. Oxford: Oxford University Press.

Searle, J.R. 1992. *The Rediscovery of the Mind*. Cambridge: MIT Press.

Strawson, G. 1994. *Mental Reality*. Cambridge: MIT Press.

16 Artificial Intelligence, Self-awareness and Creativity

16.1 SELF-CONSCIOUSNESS

Intelligence can be defined in different ways. For example, one can refer to the ability of solving new problems. Then we will say that intelligent is such a creature (it can be a brain or a technical system) which, when confronted with a new situation, can refer to its own information resources in such a way that is able to solve new problems. This ability and readiness to solve new problems is a measure of intelligence. Artificial intelligence, on the other hand, can be described as a way of implementing by technical methods such solutions or behaviours that, if they were human actions, we would call them intelligent. Intelligence applies not only to the brain, but also to the brain-body system, which regardless of whether it is artificial or natural is characterized by extremely high complexity.

Our reflections on artificial intelligence will be based on information provided by Prof. Ryszard Tadeusiewicz (biocybernetic) in an interview with Tomasz Rożek (Rożek 2011: 114).

We are able to create or rather recreate individual elements of this system, but we are not able to deal with the whole. The science that deals with these problems is cognitive science—a field bordering neuroscience, philosophy, psychology, cybernetics and computer science. Well, in cognitive science we can trace how sensual impressions, perception of the environment, perception of the inside of our body and internal organs affect our behaviour, our actions, our mind. And it turns out that we can assign all these cognitive elements specific anatomical structures within the brain. What's more, we can create mathematical models that describe these functions, and these models are increasingly used in practice. There are already image and sound recognition systems, modelled on the human eye and ear, but for information systems or robots. [...] It is known exactly which places of the cerebral cortex are responsible for the movement of each part of the body, even the little finger of the hand. In front of the so-called Rolando's fissure is an element called gyrus precentralis. There, each part of our body, including each of our fingers, has its own individual representation, one could say the place responsible for it. Before knocking on the counter, the corresponding neurons are activated in gyrus precentralis. [...] Not only that, in some circumstances these neurons are activated earlier than the conscious intention to perform some action arises. We make the decision in our consciousness that we will do something, while our biological brain already knows that we will do it. There are studies which have shown that the biological activity in those regions of the cerebral cortex that are responsible for a selected activity appears a few milliseconds earlier than the awareness of the desire to perform this activity. Man realizes that he want to do something only after his biology has already made this decision.

An experiment was once carried out where a volunteer watched the clock and had to remember the moment when he decided to press the button. Electrical activity of the volunteer cortex was recorded throughout the experiment. It turned out that the activity of neurons that started the muscles of the finger pressing the button was recorded earlier, than in the mind of the respondent there was a decision to press it.

(Rożek 2011: 117)

One can also carry out a similar experiment without using special apparatus. Let's assume that we are sitting in a chair and want to get up from it. We can get up now or at any other time. If we think about it, we will come to the conclusion that we do not know exactly when we will get up, i.e. when we will activate our muscles to do it. At some point, we get up and only then we find out. We can also do it differently, e.g. by looking at the watch and specify that from that moment we will get up in 10 s and do so. Then, however, we won't not know why we adopted the time just 10 s and why we did it at the particular moment. Generally, if we are to make a decision (yes or no), we do not know when and what decision we will make. Some additional stimulus must decide about it.

These experiments show that what we consider to be our decisions is in fact the knowledge we receive after the fact. This could indicate that we do not have free will, but all of our decisions have already been made within the changing reality according to some unknown principle. It can also be a sign of determination of reality phenomena, because it is not us (not our consciousness) who decide our actions, but the unconscious biology of the brain, associated with the material sphere of the universe. (Other arguments for determinism of the universe can be found in Chapter 20, "Binary Model of Universe".)

Another issue is the consciousness of one's own existence, which man possesses and in which we would possibly like to equip artificial intelligence.

No biological equivalent of the consciousness of one's existence was found, because this consciousness seems to be everywhere and nowhere. No biological location of the awareness of separateness from the rest of the world was found. We do not know the brain location of our subjectivity in the understanding of free will and willingness. And they tried very hard to find it. And still looking! Not only that, for psychologists are known so-called states of clear darkness. It is based on the fact that someone can act, live, actively function, contact other people and have completely turned off consciousness.

(Rożek 2011: 120)

Despite considerable efforts, neither the location nor the nature of the self-consciousness could be traced. If we wanted to create a machine similar to a human, we would not know how to equip it with a sense of its own identity.

Let's try to address this problem in the light of our considerations and consider how we can understand the sense of our own identity (self-awareness) and how it arises?

Self-awareness/consciousness appears in children between 15 and 24 months of age. Earlier thoughts apply only to the outside world, e.g. the thought/image of "a chair" or "man sitting on a chair". These thoughts identify with our mind (because there are no other thoughts in it). For self-consciousness to appear, we would have to go beyond these thoughts, i.e. juxtapose them with something. But with what, if only such thoughts are in the mind? It turns out that this is possible if we associate our thoughts with our body as the emerging object of the outside world. In other words, we will create common features of our mind with our body. When these features are strong enough (more/stronger than common features of the mind with other objects), a relationship (contrast) of the mind and body is created. If it happens, it is a strong relationship through imposition and even identity. Through this connection, with the body that connects the external and internal worlds, earlier thoughts (concerning only the external world) have become, since then, the object of (other) thoughts (next to thoughts that only concern the external world). From now on, we know that earlier thoughts belong primarily to this particular body, while before they were not assigned to anything. One can also say that these thoughts were materialized in the body (material object), thanks to which they were also separated as an object and became the object of (our) perception. This can be compared with saving the text on which we are currently working in the form of a file (e.g. in Word), which from now on forms a separate whole, to which we can refer.

I remember that when I was a child, maybe 1.5 years old, I was impressed by such an association of thoughts with the body (probably why I remember them). Before, I didn't wonder to whom my thoughts belong to; I just thought and did something. One time when I looked in the mirror, it caught my attention that when a child in the mirror moves its hand—I knew about that, I can control it, e.g. raise my hand up and the image in the mirror does the same. It was only then that I realized that the thoughts I knew and the body in the mirror belong to one person—to me. One could say that I had to "go beyond myself" to notice myself. This going beyond myself, i.e. the image in the mirror, was an additional common feature of my thoughts and body, thanks to which self-awareness probably appeared at that moment. These common features (increasing impact and contrast) could also be strengthened in other ways, e.g. I could learn that my thoughts belong to my body from my parents. This example confirms the thesis that the reason for self-awareness is a large enough quantity/ strength of common features of the mind and body (as the location of the mind). This gives the answer to two questions:

1. *Where is the biological location of the awareness of self and the rest of the world separateness?*
   This location is the place where the idea of the whole of our body, emerging from the environment, arises.
2. *How to equip artificial intelligence with self-awareness?*
   If we would like to equip the robot with self-awareness, the number of common features of the robot's body (physical elements of the robot) and its mind (artificial intelligence) should be increased by, for example, appropriate exercises associating the mind with the body, consisting in instructing

the robot to observe its movements, behaviours, etc. One could also use a mirror here. From time to time, we could check if self-awareness appears. Such a check could be, for example, a test that is also carried out with children, in which a red spot is discreetly placed on the child's nose and a mirror is given to the child. If it tries to remove the spot from its own nose and not from the image in the mirror, it means that he already has self-awareness.

The above understanding of self-awareness also explains the problem of free will, which we considered earlier, namely why we have a sense of free will. This results largely from self-awareness, i.e. the ability to control our body. In fact (as research has shown) the opposite is true: it is the "body" that affects our thoughts.

16.2   CREATIVITY

We can imitate human intelligence well in formal areas, where computers can operate according to certain rules. For example, one can build a system that will be able to reason like a doctor making a diagnosis, a judge settling a case or a stockbroker who makes the right decision by observing changes in the financial market. However, there are areas that are much more difficult to formalize and objectively describe. These include creativity and creative intelligence.

> Here the same problem arises as with the self-consciousness. We don't know where to look for structures in the brain responsible for creativity or creative intelligence, and more importantly, we also don't know how these structures work. We do not know what the essence of artistry is—that we consider the works of one painter as brilliant and another as kitsch. Which means that the works of one poet cause that people are delighted and appropriately moved by his words, while another does not. If the language of mathematics cannot describe something, we are not able to create it artificially.
>
> **(Rożek 2011: 123)**

In this work, we have largely answered the above questions; we devoted a lot of space to explain the reasons for aesthetic preferences as well as defining objective aesthetic criteria in a quantitative (formalized) manner. We will now consider how this formalization could be useful in creating artificial intelligence.

We know that the value of an artwork depends on the complexity and compression of information contained in it. In Chapter 5, Section 5.2,"Abstract Definition of Complexity", we formulated a definition of complexity which shows that the greater the information compression (i.e. the greater the degree of complexity) and the more elements this compression includes, the greater the complexity. The general model of complexity understood in this way is the complexity determined for the binary structure and expressed by the formula: $C = N^2/n$, where C—complexity, N—the number of features (distinct regularities/substructures) and n—the number of elements (zeros and ones). As one can see, this model defines the concept of complexity for a binary structure in a formal way and can be directly used wherever a given system can be expressed in a binary form. It can also be referred by analogy to other structures (not appearing in binary form), in which we deal with separate elements and we can use information compression in them. We showed this in various examples in which we analyzed contrast/complexity (e.g. in the golden ratio). As we know, this binary complexity model is a generalization of the complexity of visual interactions.

Information compression is one of the basic parameters in information technology. It is divided into lossless compression—in which the compressed form can be recovered identical to the original and lossy—in which such recovery is impossible, but the main properties are preserved. The methods of compressing information are constantly improved, because reducing the volume of files brings significant practical and economic benefits.

Information compression plays a key role in technical applications, but has not yet been noticed in the wider context as one of the fundamental issues, both for natural sciences (biology and physics) and humanities (aesthetics, epistemology, axiology, psychology and cognitive science). The concept of information compression, as we have already shown, is an important component of complexity, contrast (impact), existence, beauty, value and development. These concepts define our reality, and including in them, the complexity/compression of information allows us to go to a deeper level of understanding.

How can information compression be used in artificial intelligence systems to increase their creativity? Creativity is an ability that creates complexity, beauty and development. These values, as we know, directly depend on the compression of information. A creative system is one that produces structures with high compression. Here the question arises whether creating and improving data compression methods, which involve changing the way information is recorded so as to reduce redundancy and thus the volume of the set, is a creation. Only partially, because it is about increasing the compression of something that already exists, while creation is creating something that does not yet exist. It is easier to improve something than to build it from the beginning. That is why we do not associate the improvement of information compression methods with the creative process.

The concept of information compression in a different sense is used implicitly in the definition of algorithmic complexity (Kolmogorov), according to which the more complex system is the one whose shortest description is longer. This shortest description is nothing more than compressed information contained in a given system. Creating such a description is therefore creative. Creativity here, however, concerns not the creation of the system in question, but its definition and assessment, i.e. an auxiliary function less important than the creation of the system itself. Creating a shorter, more concise description of a given system can also be understood as improving it. Creation and creativity are associated not with assessing, defining or improving something that already exists, but creating something that does not yet exist—building a new whole/system with some ingredients. Just compressing without creating new structures is processing something already existing. It's probably why the connection between producing such a description and creativity has not been noticed. However, it was pointed out (and proved) that such a description is not computable, which means that there are no algorithms generating the shortest descriptions and, in many cases, it is not known whether the given description is the shortest or can still be shortened. This is because the creation of such (compressed) descriptions is a creative process, and therefore one that we cannot formalize. Although creating such a description is not an artistic activity, there is a certain analogy here to creating a work of art. When creating an art object, we also encounter a certain limit of creative/receptive capabilities when we are not able to increase the impact (contrast). After some time, it may turn out to be possible.

Formalization of the creative process: to understand what formalization of the creative process is, i.e. the process of building new structures with a high degree of complexity/compression of information, we will use the binary model as before. Therefore, our task will be to create such a sequence of zeros and ones, which for a given number of elements n (zeros and ones) has the highest degree of complexity (according to Abstract Complexity Definition—ACD) $D = N/n$ (N—distinct regularities/substructures), which identifies with information compression. Given the above formula, it would be easiest to generate all possible combinations of zeros and ones in the n elements and count the ratio N/n in each. Since n is the same in all sequences, it is enough to count the number of substructures—N, using the appropriate algorithm. Where N is the largest, information compression and complexity are also larger. A similar method of creation is also used by artists, irrespective of the field of creativity, often choosing from several different versions at individual stages of the artwork creation and also often using chance. One can do the same wherever the creation occurs or can be reduced to a binary or other form that allows to calculate regularities/substructures in individual concepts/proposals.

Music is one such creative field, which, as an abstract and discreet thing, is easier to formalize. That is why computers are sometimes used to compose music. There are certain rules (of composition) that can be formalized, but most of it is decided by the artist's intuition. The participation of people and their intuition is decisive because there are currently no objective aesthetic criteria that could be expressed in a mathematical (formalized) form. (The ACD of complexity in the form of a mathematical formula, which we consider to be such a criterion, shows that the measure of aesthetic value is the number of regularities/substructures that can be distinguished in a given object/composition.) How computers are used in the process of composing music?

> Musical compositions are created by superimposing the process of randomly generating certain proposals (melodic, rhythmic, instrumental, etc.) and controlling their correctness in accordance with the rules of harmony, rhythmics, rules of creating a musical genre. A piece of music, is created as a kind of filtration of what was a result of a random process.
>
> **(Rożek 2011: 125)**

The computer, by generating random suggestions, just like the composition rules, is only auxiliary, supporting the artist's intuition. There are also compositions that are entirely created by computers, but their aesthetic value is much lower than expected.

The element that distinguishes machine creativity from the work of talented people, such as genius composers, is primarily the aesthetic aspect, not the element of creativity. A song composed by a computer can be very original. Therefore, if we considered it in terms of novelty, different from what exists, we would say "Oh what a creative composer". However, what is often missing from the work created by the machine is aesthetics. Something may be original but ugly. Of course, it doesn't have to, because the random process can create everything, including unearthly beauty. But we can't teach the computer to create only pretty things, because we can't describe aesthetics with the language of mathematics, you can't define what's pretty and what's ugly.

(Rożek 2011: 126)

The above description confirms the lack of aesthetic criteria that could be used in creativity. Such criteria are the definitions of contrast and complexity, proposed in this study. As we have tried to show on many examples, these criteria apply to aesthetic and artistic objects (the difference between these concepts was explained in Section 6.3, "Distinction between Art and Beauty"). In both cases, it was important to take into account all the components of the artwork, including their context (artistic, social, etc.). For example, the value of Malevich's *Black Square* (Figure 9.23) should be seen primarily in the artistic context associated with awareness of the current situation in art. Even the most intelligent machines cannot accomplish this kind of work, unless they become indistinguishable from people. Even if that happened, it would not guarantee success, because art is difficult (also for people) and uses any objects, both physical and mental, from the area of all reality. It is much easier to formalize a less diverse area, e.g. a set of forms to create an aesthetic pattern or tones from which we want to compose a nice melody. In areas difficult to formalize, the criterion of complexity and contrast can also be useful to creators, because it makes the creative process more conscious. This does not mean that the entire creative process must be conscious, the subconscious and chance can also bring new quality to artwork—however, we can consciously decide about their use.

An example of music formalization: let's try to show a simplified example how such formalization could be done, if we wanted to compose a nice melody from a set of tones. For this purpose, we will try to translate the necessary musical elements into binary structures. These elements are: pitch and duration of tones (for simplicity, we omit pauses). Our goal is to save the melody in the form of a combination of these elements. If these elements are sequences of zeros and ones, then each combination (the melody) will also be a sequence of zeros and ones; for which we can determine the complexity (according to the mathematical formula which we already know). Then on the computer (using a simple algorithm), we will generate all possible combinations of the above-mentioned musical elements (i.e. all combinations of tones and their durations) and, using another algorithm, we will calculate the substructures (regularities) in each of them. Those combinations that have the most quantity of distinct regularities should be the most complex/melodious.

Let's assume that we have 12 tones making up the range (e.g. two-point musical range C).

The following frequencies occur in this range (given in Hertz):

c^2	523.251136
cis^2	554.365268
d^2	587.329542
dis^2	622.253974
e^2	659.255121
f^2	698.456470
fis^2	739.988853
g^2	783.990880
gis^2	830.609404
a^2	880.000009
ais^2	932.327533
b^2	987.766613
c^3	1046.502272

We want to assign to these tones sequences of zeros and ones. Their frequency (measured in Hz) is the number of vibrations (e.g. of a string) per second. Such vibrations, which are sinusoidal acoustic waves, can be written in binary form in such a way that we assign to the ones—one vibration and a specific number of zeros between the vibrations (ones) in a given tone. We can do this simplification because we are only interested in the number of vibrations per second, not their course. The frequency of tones increases from c^2 to c^3 in such a way that each subsequent value is created by multiplying the previous one by 1.06, i.e. it increases by an increasing value. As a result of this increase, the frequency of c^3 (1046.502272 Hz) is exactly twice as large as c^2 (523.251136 Hz). We must therefore determine the number of zeros for each frequency between c^2 and c^3. We will do a little simplification again and take the multiplier value not 1.06 but 1. It means that every next frequency will increase by the same amount. In our binary notation, an increase in frequency means a decrease in the number of zeros between ones. Let's assume that the smallest increase in frequency (i.e. by one degree) corresponds to a decrease in the number of zeros by one zero. The number of zeros for each frequency should now be calculated. Let us assume the number of zeros for c^3 equal to x and for c^2 the value 2x. Between these values, the frequency increases 11 times by one zero. So we have the relationship: x + 11 = 2x, hence x = 11 corresponds to the tone c^3, while the tone of c^2 corresponds to 2x = 22 (zeros between ones). So we can write the subsequent tone in the binary form.

c^2	10000000000000000000001000000000000000000000001000000000000000000000001...
cis^2	1000000000000000000001000000000000000000001000000000000000000001...
d^2	100000000000000000001000000000000000000010000000000000000001...
dis^2	10000000000000000001000000000000000001000000000000000001...
e^2	1000000000000000001000000000000000010000000000000001...
f^2	100000000000000001000000000000001000000000000001...
fis^2	10000000000000001000000000000010000000000001...
g^2	1000000000000001000000000000100000000000001...
gis^2	100000000000010000000000001000000000001...
a^2	10000000000010000000000100000000001...
ais^2	1000000000010000000000100000000001...
b^2	100000000010000000000100000000001...
c^3	100000000001000000000100000000001...

We can see that the frequency of vibrations (of ones) is the smallest for the tone of c^2, and it gradually increases, reaching the value twice as high for the tone c^3 (octave). Such analogous recording of tones also takes into account their frequency and duration. These two quantities are enough to compose a simple melodic piece of music such as the carol *Silent Night*. We assign 4 times to these 12 tones, e.g. a half note (1 s), a quarter note (0.5 s), a quarter-dotted (0.75 s) and an eighth note (0.25 s). Now we should calculate the duration of the whole melody. The frequency c^3 is about 1,000 Hz, the distance between ones (vibration period) is therefore 0.001 s which corresponds to 11 zeros plus one (because we also include the one in the vibration period and assign it the same duration as zero). The duration of zero/one is therefore 0.001/12 = 0.00008 s. Therefore, the half note will correspond to 1/0.00008 = 12,500 (zeros and ones), quarter-dotted with 9,375, quarter note—6,250 zeros and eight—3,125 (ones and zeros).

For example, the c^3 tone lasting a half note will look like this: 100000000001000 0000000100000000001 ... 00001 (12,500 zeros and ones in total).

The c^2 tone lasting half note will look like this: 10000000000000000000000010 0000000000000000 ... 01 (12,500 zeros and ones in total).

Etc.

Having records of all tones and their durations, we can generate all their combinations (i.e. all combinations that can be obtained, having 12 tones and 4 times of their duration) within the assumed melody duration, e.g. 100 s, and then in all these combinations to count the distinct regularities. The combination where there is the most quantity of the regularities should be the most melodious. There are a lot of these combinations, so one could limit their number by imposing appropriate boundary conditions, e.g. limit the selection of tones only to the C major key or take instead of 4 tones only 3. One can also go in another direction and take into account more parameters, such as pauses, other ranges, counterpoint and volume.

In the above example, it was primarily about showing the possibilities of creating a binary record of a musical piece which is identified with this record-code, where binary structures are not conventional codes, but physical representations of real music. Such a record allows, therefore, to use the computer's computational capabilities to compose music in a much more effective way than if we had assigned contractual codes to the tones and their duration. Then we could make aesthetic assessment of individual combinations only to a very limited extent—by listening to all versions, which could be much above a billion.

The method of binary recording of music presented here is a special record in which various physical qualities, such as pitch and duration, are identified in their binary recording. This record can therefore be treated as a binary music model. A similar binary model, but modelling visual interactions, was used to formulate the definition of complexity (which we use here for aesthetic assessment) and the definition of being (reality and universe). In Chapter 20, "Binary Model of Universe", we also will identify the binary structure with the universe. Because now we identified the binary structure with music, we can also identify the universe with music. We could (easily) identify the binary musical model with music itself because of its abstract character. Thanks to this, it is possible to compose by analyzing the binary structures, using computers.

Let's look at this analysis in more detail. The pitch and duration of a tone are two different and basic qualities that make up the music. These qualities are special because they are measured by the same measure—by time. The pitch of the tone depends on time (period of vibration of the acoustic wave) and also the duration of the tone depends on time. These qualities have strong common and differentiating features, so they create a high contrast. It follows that the tone itself (which is the contrast) is aesthetically attractive and even more so an appropriate combination of sounds that creates a more complex contrast. We are currently creating music by combining sounds intuitively so as to obtain the greatest complexity. This means that we intuitively create different combinations of sounds and we intuitively evaluate them. Both can be done for us by a computer, but the way it does it is interesting. The computer first creates all combinations of binary tones and thus sets together not single zeros and ones, but their structures/systems (tones), while the assessment of these combinations of tones (melodies) is already made on the basis of analysis of the entire structure consisting of single zeros and ones (where only zeros and ones are considered). This greatly simplifies the analysis, because we do not need to separately analyze the pitches and their duration.

The above binary formalization takes into account all aspects that affect the aesthetic value and the feeling of pleasure such as good organization of musical pieces, multiplicity in unity and richness of meanings/features, in short: complexity.

PLEASURE OF SOUNDS PERCEPTION

Considering the issue of musical creation, one cannot omit the psychophysiological aspect based on the perception of harmonic and disharmonic sounds, i.e. consonance and dissonance described as follows:

> In music, **consonance** and **dissonance** are categorizations of simultaneous or successive sounds. Within the Western tradition, consonance is typically associated with sweetness, pleasantness, and acceptability; dissonance is associated with harshness, unpleasantness, or unacceptability although this depends also on familiarity and musical expertise (Lahdelma and Eerola 2020). The terms form a structural dichotomy in which they define each other by mutual exclusion: a consonance is what is not dissonant, and a dissonance is what is not consonant. However, a finer consideration shows that the distinction forms a gradation, from the most consonant to the most dissonant (Schoenberg 1978, p. 21). As Hindemith stressed, "The two concepts have never been completely explained, and for a thousand years the definitions have varied" (Hindemith 1942: 85).
> **(https://en.wikipedia.org/wiki/Consonance_and_dissonance)**

Let's try to explain these terms using the contrast definition. Consonances may include:

Perfect Consonances

Unisons (frequencies ratio 1:1): the sounds are presented as a digital model. The duration of one vibration is equivalent to two digits in each sound (10 and 10).

1010101010101010101010101010101010
1010101010101010101010101010101010

Octaves (2:1): the duration of one vibration is equivalent to two digits in the first sound: 10 and four digits in the second sound: 1000.

1010101010101010101010101010101010
1000100010001000100010001000

Perfect fifths (3:2): the duration of one vibration is equivalent to three digits in the first sound: 100 and two digits in the second sound: 10.

100100100100100100100100100001
1010101010101010101010101010101010

Perfect fourths (4:3): the duration of one vibration is equivalent to four digits in the first sound: 1000 and three digits in the second sound: 100.

100010001000100010001000100010
100100100100100100100100001

Imperfect consonances

Major sixths (5:3), major thirds (5:4), minor thirds (6:5) and minor sixths (8:5).
  Dissonances may include:
  Tritones, minor seconds and major sevenths. Consider minor seconds:
  Second (13:12): the duration of one vibration is equivalent to 13 digits in the first sound: 1000000000000 and 12 digits in the second sound: 100000000000.

10000000000001000000000000010000000000000100000000000100000000
10000000000010000000000010000000000010000000000010000000000001

We notice a certain regularity here, which consists in increasing numbers in frequency proportions from the smallest (unisons 1:1) to the largest (minor seconds 13:12). We can also see that as these numbers increase, the number of ones matching in both sounds decreases: in unisons, it is the highest (all matching—the vibrations occur simultaneously), and in dissonance, there is no longer any matching in the area in question. Vibrations occurring simultaneously should be treated as common features of both sounds under consideration.

  More common features make greater contrast and more pleasant sound, confirming the principle of contrast.

REFERENCES

Hindemith, P. 1942. *The Craft of Musical Composition*, vol. I, translated by Arthur Mendel. New York: Associated Music Publishers.

Lahdelma, I. & Eerola, T. 2020. Cultural Familiarity and Musical Expertise Impact the Pleasantness of Consonance/Dissonance but Not Its Perceived Tension. *Scientific Reports* 10: 8693.

Rożek, T. 2011. *Nauka po prostu—wywiady z wybitnymi* [Just Science—Interviews with Outstanding Scientists]. Warszawa: Demart SA.

Schoenberg, A. 1978. *Theory of Harmony*. Berkeley, LA: University of California Press.

17 Contrast as Being

17.1 CONTEMPORARY UNDERSTANDING OF BEING

In philosophy, being means the existence of a thing. Anything that exists has being. Ontology is the branch of philosophy that studies being. Being is a concept encompassing objective and subjective features of reality and existence. Anything that partakes in being is also called a "being", though often this usage is limited to entities that have subjectivity (as in the expression "human being"). The notion of "being" has, inevitably, been elusive and controversial in the history of philosophy, beginning in Western philosophy with attempts among the pre-Socratics to deploy it intelligibly. The first effort to recognize and define the concept came from Parmenides, who famously said of it that "what is-is". Common words such as "is", "are" and "am" refer directly or indirectly to being.

(https://en.wikipedia.org/wiki/Being)

The grand achievement of classical metaphysics was the theory of being of Saint Thomas Aquinas. In this theory, being is distinguished in the distributive sense (that is, everything that exists in any way—an object) and being in a collective sense (that is, a set of all that exists). If we recognize the identity between the expression "being" and the expression "this -- what exists in any way", then we can distinguish two aspects of being: essential (essence)—"this what" and existential (existence)— "exists". The specificity of understanding the concept of being depends on how we understand individual fragments of the concept, i.e. meaning of particles "this", "what" and "exists". If we divide the understanding of the concept of being because of what the particle "this" means, i.e. the scope of the concept of being, then it stands out: (1) being in the distributive sense ("this" is a specific object); (2) being in a collective sense ("this" is a collection of these objects); and (3) being as everything ("this" points to an unspecified everything).

Since the concept of being is defined by the concept of existence, in order to define/understand being, one should first define the concept of existence:

Existence is the ability of an entity to interact with physical or mental reality. In philosophy, it refers to the ontological property of being.
(https://en.wikipedia.org/wiki/Existence)

In this definition, the term "interaction" appears, which also requires the definition:

Interaction is a kind of action that occur as two or more objects have an effect upon one another. The idea of a two-way effect is essential in the concept of interaction, as opposed to a one-way causal effect.
(https://en.wikipedia.org/wiki/Interaction)

In this definition, the concept of action appears, which also needs to be defined. Existing definitions describe specific examples of action, but do not explain what action is:

> In physics, action is an attribute of the dynamics of a physical system from which the equations of motion of the system can be derived.
>   **(https://en.wikipedia.org/wiki/Action_(physics))**

The definition of elementary particle interactions is considered to be the most fundamental definition of interaction in physics:

> In physics, a fundamental interaction (depending on the nature of the interaction, it might also be called a fundamental force) is a process by which elementary particles interact with each other. An interaction is often described as a physical field, and is mediated by the exchange of gauge bosons between particles. For example, the interaction of charged particles takes place through the mediation of electromagnetic fields, whereas beta decay occurs by means of the weak interaction. An interaction is fundamental when it cannot be described in terms of other interactions. There are four known fundamental interactions in nature: The electromagnetic, strong, weak and gravitational interactions. The weak and electromagnetic interactions are unified in electroweak theory, which is unified with the strong force in the standard model.
>   **(https://en.wikipedia.org/wiki/Interaction)**

The above definition presents current knowledge about interactions of particles in the micro-world, but does not explain what the interaction is in general sense. We have different examples of interactions, but we still do not know what their essence is—a common feature of all interactions (mental and physical). There is no clarification (defining and verbalizing) of our intuitions regarding the concept of interaction.

17.2   DEFINITION OF BEING

The definition of contrast, *in the general sense, what affects us is contrast, or tension resulting from the impacts (effects) of common and differentiating features of objects/structures. Contrast grows stronger as the number/strength of common and differentiating features held by contrasting objects increases*, tells us what all kinds of interactions between objects depend on (what is their essence). Because everything we experience is an interaction (in the broadest sense), the principle of contrast should be considered the most general law on which our perception of reality is based. Let us now consider how the principle of contrast can be understood in relation to all objects of reality, also existing independently of us.

Every existing object (being) must have common and differentiating features. If it had only common (which would amount to one feature), it would be something uniform, which could not be said to exist. If it had only differing features, they could not appear together as an object. In this case, it would also be possible to consider only one selected feature, because there would be no contact with others. It follows that the simplest object would have to consist of at least two elements that would have one common and differentiating feature (this is related to the so-called binding problem mentioned above, i.e. combining various features inside objects). The simplest object (which was already mentioned) is the combination of one with zero, i.e. a combination of any state different from zero with zero or nothingness. A common feature is to be understood as closeness (e.g. in time) or overlapping of both states. Overlapping can be explained as follows: if we were dealing only with the very one (single state), we could not distinguish it from zero (because there would be no change and no reference), just as we could not extract the red colour if everything was red.

It follows from the above reasoning that both *the simplest object and every other being are the effect of common and differentiating features, i.e. the effect of contrast.*

It is proved that the simplest elements 1 and 0 can create structures simulating any complex physical processes/objects (and thus the whole reality), which Ludwig von Bertalanffy first noticed in *Theory of Systems* (Bertalanffy 1968) and is currently confirmed by many theoreticians (including Stephen Wolfram, Seth Lloyd, Ed Fredkin, Tom Toffoli, Frank Tipler and Jurgen Schmidhuber). It follows that the binary structure can be treated as the simplest model of reality, which also takes into account all its possible objects. (This model will be discussed in detail in Chapter 20, "Binary Model of Universe".) Therefore, each cognitive process leads to a binary structure as the basic level of cognition. Further exploration could apply only to the elements themselves, i.e. ones and zeros, which, however, as the simplest mental elements/objects, are already unknowable.

The basic being, i.e. the overlapping of one and zero, is autonomous and necessary because, just as there is no "one" without "zero", there is no "zero" without "one" (they cannot be isolated separately). Hence, the logical possibility of spontaneous creation of all structures of reality. Such reality/universe is self-sufficient and self-explanatory and limit our understanding (we cannot mentally go beyond it in a logical way).

17.3 EXISTING CONCEPTS OF BEING

To bring our concept closer, we will now carry out a brief description of the theory of being in the history of philosophy, which correspond with ours based on *History of Philosophy*, by Władysław Tatarkiewicz (1981).

Democritus: if we wanted to look for similarities to the concept of being presented here in the history of philosophy, we would have to start with the philosophy of nature of Ancient Greece and, in particular, with atomism, which in the most advanced form presented Democritus. Atomism assumed that matter consists of atoms, that is, as the Greek term itself says "indivisible particles". The theory of atoms had four basic theses:

1. All nature consists only of atoms. Of them are composed all bodies in nature.
2. Atoms have only quantitative properties (they do not have qualitative). The properties that distinguish one atom from another are reduced to shape,

position and order. These few, and only, geometric properties of atoms explain all properties of complex bodies.

3. The common property of atoms is a movement that is eternal like the atoms themselves and does not need to be given to them by any external factor. The movement consists only in changing the place in space and is the only form of transformation that atoms undergo.

4. Atoms move in a vacuum. The vacuum exists because it is necessary to explain the movement. Movement is possible thanks to the existing free space (vacuum) in which they can move.

Similarities:

Atomists for the first time attempted to explain all qualitative properties with quantitative properties. In relation to previous views, according to which the components of nature were qualitatively different, they explained their conception with greater simplicity, intelligibility and computability, which was important from the scientific point of view. They also reduced the number of atomic features to three geometric features: shape, location and order. This theory, assuming the existence of atoms and vacuum, for the first time, also assumed the discontinuity of matter. The pursuit of simplicity, discontinuity and quantitative properties brings this theory closer to the binary model.

Pythagoreans: they are the most important reference here because of the simplest and most abstract way of understanding existence. They dealt with geometry, arithmetic and acoustics, contributing significantly to their development. They found that the cause of the sound is movement, and that the musical sounds show mathematical regularity. Harmonious sounds correspond to the simplest numerical relations: half of the string gives an octave and two-thirds of the fundamental tone a quint. In all these studies, the number was dominant, which was significant for their philosophical views.

> Mathematical and acoustic inquiries determined the general philosophical concept of Pythagoreans. Finding in them everywhere a number as a decisive factor in the properties of things, seeing how it creates spatial figures, hearing how the harmonies of sounds are formed through it, they were so overwhelmed by its power that the question of what the world was made of and what is its main factor was no longer answered by either "water" or "air" as the Ionic people did, but they answered: number. For the world owes its shape and order to it, it is a living principle and a manager. "Being impressed by math", says Aristotle, "they thought that its principles are the principles of all being, because in it the numbers are obviously the first thing, and they thought that they see in numbers numerous similarities with what is and what is becoming, more numerous than in earth, fire, water ... they considered numbers as the first thing in all nature, the roots of numbers for the roots of being, the all heavens for harmony and number".

(Tatarkiewicz 1981: 1, 56)

Similarities:

Our model of being/universe is also a number, but a binary one, that is, written in the simplest possible way (using only two elements). In the following chapters, we will see how this number can be used to model the structures/objects of reality.

An important similarity is also the relationship between numbers and music. Pythagoreans have found in numbers the essence of harmony of individual sounds and their chords, e.g. "in the chord C, G, the length of the strings (1, 2/3, 1/2) creates a special proportion, which they called 'harmonious' $(1:1/2) = (1-2/3):(2/3-1/2)$" (Tatarkiewicz 1981: 56). In our considerations (Chapter 16, "Artificial Intelligence, Self-awareness and Creativity"), we showed how music can be written in the form of a binary number and how the melodiousness/harmoniousness criterion of a musical piece can be determined numerically.

Spinoza: Spinoza's philosophical views have their main source in the pantheistic metaphysics of such classics as Plotinus and John Scotus Eriugena, as well as in Thomas Hobbes's mechanistic views and the Cartesian theory of cognition. He often justified his theses by showing the inconsistency of Descartes views:

> In the philosophy of Descartes, he condemned its dualism: the duality of God and the world, thought and extension, the soul and body, freedom and mechanism. He tried to overcome the dualism based on Descartes own assumptions; from his definition of a substance (substance is what exists by itself and what can be understood by itself), he asserted that the substance is only one, and identifies with God. Because for something to exists through itself, it can not be anything limited; it must be infinite, and the infinite substance is God. The substance can not be created, because then it would have a cause and would exist by the cause, and not by itself. There can be no substance besides God. God or substance: these are two names of the same thing. Hence it follows that the universe can not exist outside of God, but only in God. Both the world of things and the world of thought are not self-existent, but they are symptoms of the self-existent, i.e. God. They are not outside of God, and therefore God is not outside of them. God, or nature: these are two names of one thing. Through this pantheism, the duality of God and the world was to be overcome.
>
> **(Tatarkiewicz 1981: 2, 71)**

Spinoza also recognized universal determinism—in the world there are eternal laws in force; everything that is going on is necessary; there is no freedom or chance: "All nature is a mechanism; and man, his deeds and works, society, state, all culture—all this is also a necessary product of mechanically developing nature" (Tatarkiewicz 1981: 2, 72).

Similarities:

From our concept, similarly to the above, it follows that being is self-existent. The difference lies in the fact that Spinoza explains this self-existence with the self-existence of God who identifies with the world (pantheism). Our considerations show that self-existence is a logical necessity resulting from the limitation of our mind.

This necessity may or may not be associated with the presence of God. Our concept is also monistic and deterministic, as will be explained in more detail in Chapter 20, "Binary Model of Universe".

Hegel: he was an idealist—identified thought with being:

> It is therefore necessary to seek the original nature of being in thought. And it must be assumed that being as a thought is logical in nature. The constituent of being is the same as the component of logical thought—concept. And the generality constituting the essence of concepts is also the essence of being; everything what is individual, it is only its secondary manifestation. Faithful to this universalist view, Hegel put emphasis on general property in every field of phenomena as essential and omitted individual.
>
> **(Tatarkiewicz 1981, 2: 213)**

For the superior law of logic, he considered dialectical law, consisting in, that every thesis corresponded to the antithesis, which combined into synthesis. Hegel turned this law into the law of being:

> The process of moving from thesis to antithesis was for him a matrix of not only reasoning, but also real development. Behind every form of being, its negation follows; therefore, contrary to popular belief, the contradiction is not only not excluded from reality, but is its deepest nature.
>
> **(Tatarkiewicz 1981: 214)**

Similarities:

Hegel's philosophy is significant for us because it assumes the logical equivalence of thoughts and things. Our concept also transfers the logical existence of being from mind to reality: it intellectually extracts the basic components of mind and refers them (by analogy) to the basic components of the universe.

There is also some convergence of Hegel's dialectic law with our understanding of contrast. Both concepts explain development in a similar way. In both of them, there are three elements: in dialectics—thesis, antithesis and synthesis; in contrast— two contrasting objects and their combination, that is, a combination of their differing features (which can also be considered as a synthesis). The difference is that the law of contrast is more general and universal because dialectical contradictions do not occur in nature (outside the mind): it is difficult to say that, for example, green grass and red flower are contradictory; contrast, however, includes such a combination. Contrast can take into account many different features of contrasting objects; the contradiction, however, concerns the extreme values (opposites) within one trait, e.g. heat-cold, light-dark, etc.

Aristotle: he made the characterization of the concept of being, which laid the foundations for classical metaphysics:

1. Being is the most general notion, because everything that is, is a being. Nothing exists that does not fall within the scope of this concept.

2. Being is an indefinite concept, because its content is an abstraction from specific features.
3. Being is an indefinable concept, because there is no kind to which this concept should belong.

Similarities:

This characteristic is up to date, and being is still understood as the most general, indefinite and indefinable. Understanding of being as a contrast, however, says something more about being than "that it is an abstraction from specific features". Namely, it says that *being is a complex concept—a contrast, that is, a tension-interaction of common and differentiating features (of any object/objects).*

To conclude, in this chapter, we have set out the contemporary understanding of being, showing that there is no clarification of our intuitions regarding the concept of interaction and being. We then presented our own concept of being based on the definition of contrast, concluding that both the simplest object and every other being are the effect of common and differentiating features, i.e. the effect of contrast. Taking into account that the simplest object-contrasts are (for our mind) elements 1 and 0, and that these elements can create structures simulating any complex physical processes/objects (and thus the whole reality), a hypothesis has emerged that the binary structure can be treated as the simplest model of reality. This chapter ends with a brief description of the theory of being in the history of philosophy, which corresponds with ours.

REFERENCES

Bertalanffy, L. 1968. *General Systems Theory.* New York: G. Brazilier.
Tatarkiewicz, W. 1981. *Historia Filozofii* [*History of Philosophy*] Warszawa: PWN.

18 Contrast and Perception of Reality

It has already been pointed out that common features connect contrasting objects/ structures, producing as a result new structures with different levels of complexity. Let us now consider what differentiating features of connected objects are. It appears that these features are also common features/connections in relation to yet other objects that are present either within or without the area (such as a painting) under examination, as shown on Figure 18.1. Here we see the following drawings: a large square, a large circle, a small circle and a small head of a man.

Consider the contrast between the large square and the large circle. Their common feature is size, while the differentiating features are the shape of the square and that of the circle. Moreover, the shape of the circle is a feature held in common by the large and small circles, while their differentiating feature is a different size. In turn, the size of the small circle is a common feature of the small circle and the head drawing, with meaning as their differentiating feature. The circle is a geometric form and the head—an illusion of a real thing. Furthermore, the head drawn on the painting and an actual head outside the picture have in common the feature of visual similarity and are differentiated by meaning: the real thing and an illusion, while the common feature of the square from the painting and of, for example, the table placed outside the picture is shape (square), and their differentiating feature is meaning: a geometrical form and a real thing. By connecting additional elements/structures in this manner, we would be able, theoretically, to include in our perception the entire reality, and each connection made would involve greater or lesser contrast/ development. We can talk about embracing all reality because all the elements of reality are connected by common features; there are no detached elements (because if they were detached, they would not belong to reality). Here emerges a coherent picture/model of reality perception as a network of connections between its elements.

Let's consider whether this model (of reality perceived by us) could be identified with the model of reality itself. Considering the earlier arguments that unify the mind with the body, we assume that we can consider the visual model of reality perception described above as a model of reality itself. In this model (Figure 18.1) the image (elements in a rectangle) could symbolize our mind and what is beyond the rectangle—the outside world. We see that the principle of contrast applies everywhere equally, regardless of whether contrast is created by concepts, features, meanings, forms or material objects—things. All these (distinguishing in some way) elements are treated as structures of reality (including man and his mind), which enter into relations (contrasts) with each other creating more or less complex structures.

This visual model explains in an illustrative way how the structures of reality are created. It is more realistic than the binary model proposed in the previous chapter

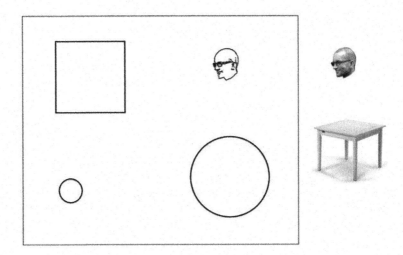

FIGURE 18.1 Features that differentiate contrasting objects are at the same time features held in common (connections) with other objects that are present either within or without the area (such as a painting) under examination.

and should be understood as an intermediate link between the image/model of reality as the zero-one structure and the reality perceived directly. The aim of introducing such an intermediate link was to facilitate the imagination of the transition (analogy) between the binary model and reality. Let's try to change (translate) objects and their contrasts from the visual model (Figure 18.1) into binary structures. However, this change should only be treated as a suggestion, because with full or even similar correspondence, they would have to have much more elements and be much more complicated (as will be discussed later).

1. Consider the contrast of the large square with the large circle. Their common feature is the size, and differentiating features are the shape of the square and shape of the circle.

   Let us assume that the large square corresponds to the following structure: 1111000011110000. Let us assume that the big circle corresponds to the following structure: 1100111100001100.

   Common features: number of elements, 4 ones and 4 zeros. Differentiating features: arrangement of elements.

2. Consider the contrast of the large circle with the small circle. Their common feature is the shape and distinguishing feature is size.

   Let us assume that the following structure corresponds to the big circle: 1100111100001100. Let us assume that the following structure corresponds to the small circle: 10110010.

   Common features: the elements in the large circle are exactly doubled elements of the small circle. Differentiating features: number of elements.

3. Consider the contrast of the small circle and the drawing of the head. Their common feature is the size and differentiating feature is the meaning.

The following structure corresponds to the small circle: 10110010.

The following structure corresponds to the drawing of the head: 10010110. Common features: 2 ones, 2 zeros, single one and single zero. Differentiating features: layout and complexity (the number of distinguishing substructures is greater in the drawing of a head).

4. Consider the contrast between the head and the real head. Their common features are the size and the visual structure, and their distinctive feature is the meaning.

The following structure corresponds to the drawing of a head: 10010110.

The following structure corresponds to the real head: 10010110110 00011110010010110. Common features: 2 ones, 2 zeros, single one and single zero. Differentiating features: number of elements, layout and complexity (number of substructures).

In the above examples, one can notice a certain analogy between the visual objects and the binary structures assigned to them as well as their contrasts. In Figure 18.1, we showed how to connect individual objects through common features, e.g. the drawn head in the picture and a real head outside the picture through visual similarity (colour, shape, structure, size). In fact, in this connection, the observer's mind would mediate, first connecting to one object, then the other and then comparing/juxtaposing them in the imagination. Let us analyze step by step the connection of the real head (material object) with the observer's mind.

Light falls on the head, and the reflecting photons carry information about the surface structure of the object, which is first "translated" (encoded) into energy and the number of photons and then some of them falling on the retina is translated into the structure of electrical impulses in the brain, which in turn is already directly perceived as a colour. So we see here that the connection of the observer's mind and object is not direct and consists of several connections (links). The observer does not realize all these transitions, taking them altogether as a colour (e.g. red)— belonging to the perceived object or (more consciously) as a common feature of the object and the observer's imagination/mind. This common feature, conventionally called colour, should be understood as a feature consisting of several features with a specific energy structure, located in space and time. A part of this feature directly related to the object (head) is the feature/structure of the surface of this object (types of atoms, their arrangement etc.) that reflects photons with a specific energy (in this case, the energy/wavelength corresponding to the red light). In turn, a part of this feature directly related to the mind/imagination is the appropriate structure of electrical impulses in the brain that evokes/unifies with the feeling of a given colour. I treat each of these parts (of the complex feature considered) as a material part-feature of the considered objects (perceived and perceiving), in accordance with the earlier postulate of the need for energy in each structure.

In Chapter 14, "Contrast as Cognition" (Figure 14.1), we showed how various visual features, by overlapping, are combined in objects (S1 and S2). Let's demonstrate how this connection would look in a binary structure. Consider the following structure:

1011010010, we can extract the following substructures-features in it:

1. Zeros.
2. Ones.
3. Double elements (combine double ones and double zeros).
4. Double ones (combine ones and double elements).
5. Double zeros (combine zeros and double elements).

We had similar connections in Section 4.3, "Binary Model of Visual Interactions", where individual substructures-features created contrasts of black and white squares. Combinations of binary features can also be implemented by overlapping in a different way. Consider the following structures:

1. 10110111000101101110001011011111 (repeating increasing sequence)
2. 10000000000100000000010000000 (single elements)
3. 00110000000001100000000110000 (double elements)
4. 00000111000000001110000000111 (triple components)

The structure/feature (1) was created here by combining (overlapping) structures (2), (3) and (4). The above examples suggest that binary structures can model reality structures by analogy. Such a possibility, in both natural sciences (physics) and humanities (philosophy), has not been taken into account so far. Currently, binary structures are commonly used as codes (contractual signs), for example, in telecommunications or computer simulations. There is more about these analogies in Chapter 20, "Binary Model of Universe".

19 Definition of Information

19.1 STRUCTURAL AND SHANNON'S INFORMATION

Information (like complexity) does not have a general unifying definition to date. There are many definitions (more or less general) and their interpretations in existing literature. We consider here only two of them regarded as the most important, and we point to their essential common and differentiating features, which haven't been taken into account so far. Including this knowledge would avoid many misunderstandings regarding their applications. This is Shannon's definition formulated for the needs of telecommunications and the so-called structural definition. There are disputes about the generality and scope of applications of these definitions:

> The most important seems to be the dispute, in which the dividing line runs between the understanding of information in terms of selection (Hartley, Shannon, Turing, along with the whole mainstream research) and the understanding of information in terms of structure (Belkin, Robertson, Jacob, Young, Thom). The question remains: is a conceptual system possible, in which information is defined in such a way that the existing concepts lying on opposite sides of the dividing line become its special cases?
>
> **(Schroeder 2015)**

We will try to understand more deeply the essence of the definitions listed here and their relationship. Information in the most general terms can be defined as Aristotle understood it—as a form that is the source of knowledge (in contrast to the first matter—*prote hyle* that is unknowable). *Such a general definition should take into account the selective and structural aspect of information, i.e. contain the definition of Shannon information—as elimination of uncertainty (by choosing the right element from a given set) and a structural definition—where information is a distinguishing element, feature, form or regularity in the structure of an object/ system/structure.* It could be seen that the structural definition agrees with the general definition here. It remains to check if Shannon's definition is its special case.

Information as an element of a set or a collection (i.e. an object of low/loose integration) is also a feature of this set but of a special character—namely, it does not create relationships with other features except that which determines its affiliation to a given set, i.e. the common feature of these elements (e.g. the same number of zeros and ones "n"—if we consider a set of n-element sequences). The elements of the set/ collection are thus well defined and distinguished entities, such as, sugar cubes in a box, individual particles in a gas and their states (hence the correlation of Shannon definition with thermodynamics) or codes in code tables. Therefore, collections (of information) are used in telecommunications because their elements have 100% distinguishability, which eliminates the possibility of an error (in their selection and transmission). However, the set/collection is also a special case of structure, although it is a structure of loosely connected elements, i.e. with a small degree of integration. In more organized structures, relations between features are diverse and more complex, and individual features (information) are distinguished to a different extent, which excludes their suitability for telecommunications needs. It can therefore be said that Shannon's information is also a structural information, i.e. a feature of an object, but an object-collection (such as a register of codes), i.e. in which the information-elements are isolated completely (in 100%). It is the essential feature that distinguishes it from structural information (which is all possible information, because every information has a structure).

The fundamental difference between these two types of information lies in the way they are interpreted. Shannon's information is interpreted as one of the possible states of the system and its information measure depends not on the structure, but on the number of possible states of the system. (This measure is the number of information bits, which is determined by the binary logarithm of the number of possible states.) If, for example, the system is a sequence of zeros and ones with the total number of elements n = 3, the set of all states of this system will be the following sequences: 000, 001, 010, 011, 100, 101, 110, 111. The number of these sequences/states is $8 = 2^3$. Each of them contains the amount of information $I = \log 2^3 = 3$ (bits). This way of determining the information content is convenient for information processing, e.g. when searching code registers. Searching for a given code requires (in the least favourable case) comparing it with all codes of a given register (a set of codes). Each such comparison is a physical process and requires a specific portion of energy. So we can calculate the total search energy. Structural information is not interpreted as one of the possible states of the system, but as each distinguishing feature of a given system, which can be assigned 1 bit of information. The information content of a given system is therefore equal to the number of features/bits it contains.

Can we consider Shannon's information as a special case of structural definition? As an element of a set (i.e. a special type of structure), yes. When it comes to interpretation, the difference is essential here. This definition has been formulated for the needs of telecommunications and its use outside the technical context leads to misunderstandings. The structural definition is not suitable for technical applications but is useful in all other cases.

For a better understanding of the relationship of these definitions, we will use an example. Consider the binary structure from Figure 4.5a—10010110, which, as we counted, has eight features (distinguished regularities/orders of zeros and ones). For the needs of telecommunications, however, these features/information are of little use because they do not distinguish themselves equally (some are less distinctive, others more, which makes their selection difficult). In telecommunications, the sequence of zeros and ones, e.g. 10010110, is treated not as an object/structure but as a selected state from a set of all possible states of the system (a collection-object). This set consists of all possible sequences of zeros and ones with the same total number of zeros and ones n (this number is their common feature), i.e. all possible combinations of zeros and ones for a number (n = 8). The number of such combinations is 2^8 and the structure 10010110 is one of them, next to, e.g., 10101010, 11101101 and 10001000. Each of the sequences/features/information is distinguished equally and in 100% so that they can be used for coding. Besides, each of them informs about how many such sequences contain a set (i.e. 2^n), which is an important message when searching in such a set.

19.2   ENERGY—INFORMATION RELATIONSHIP

There are conflicting views on the subject of energy-information relations to this day. Some theorists believe that information can be identified with energy, and others think in the opposite way. For example, Carl Friedrich von Weizsäcker in his book *The Unity of Nature* (Weizsäcker 1978: 426–427) states the identity of form and matter, measuring them—information (measuring the amount of form) and mass (measuring the amount of matter). This understanding, however, is valid only for information defined by Shannon, understood (as defined by Shannon) as an element of the collection, where every information corresponds to a single, specific portion of energy—needed for recording or transmission of the information. However, it does not apply where (distinguishing) elements form a coherent organized structures (as a result of relationships between the elements). Here the energy of recording and the transmission of information are identified with the energy contained in the structure of a given information (number of ones) and may be different for different information. *In such well-organized objects/structures (e.g. such as the brain), thanks to information compression and the associated energy savings, the amount of information per unit of energy is greater than in less complex/organized objects* (as also was discussed in Chapter 6, "Contrast as Compression of Information").

We must point out here that the amount of information per unit of energy resulting from the compression (energy savings) of information should not be confused with the amount of information per unit of energy resulting from the size of the portion of energy used to record/transmit the information, for example, information contained in the 1010 structure can be recorded/transmitted using different portions of energy according to practical needs.

Energy is necessary for the existence and transmission of information (matter/energy, speaking Aristotelian is the possibility of form). No form exists without energy—hence the view of some theoreticians (Weizsäcker) that information identifies with energy—but not all information requires the same amount of energy—hence the view of some theoreticians (Wiener) that information is not energy.

Thanks to the organization of form (that is, compression and complexity of information), we can obtain more information with the same energy. This can be seen in Figure 4.5 where, with the same number of ones (4) corresponding to the number of energy portions/quanta, the structure in Figure 4.5a contains 8 features, structure in Figure 4.5b only 1 and structure in Figure 4.5c contains 3. The above explanation is settled by the dispute regarding the information-energy relationship. It has become possible due to the inclusion of the role of form organization, i.e. the compression and complexity of information. Although the concept of information compression (lossy and lossless) is now well defined in the area of information theory, it does not function in other fields of knowledge such as epistemology, aesthetics, axiology, biology or physics. It seems that the inclusion of information compression in these areas would allow us to understand many unclear issues, some of which we have tried to explain in this work.

19.3   THE VALUE OF INFORMATION

Understanding what complexity and organization are also allows to understand how highly organized structures/objects such as living organisms are created and what is their evolution and development. Development as well as contrast, complexity and compression of information (that is, the economy resulting from energy savings) can be identified with the value in general, hence with the value of information.

Valuable information is the essential characteristic of a given system, which we take into account in the description of the system and analyses of its relationship (contrasts) with other systems (as we did in the attached examples). The value of information can also be identified with its meaning, which can also be more or less valuable-complex):

> Although meaning is hard to define, it is one of the most powerful features of information. The basic idea of information is that one physical system—a digit, a letter, a word, a sentence—can be put into correspondence with another physical system. The information stands for the thing. Two fingers can be used to represent two cows, two people, two mountains, two ideas. A word can stand for anything (anything for which we have a word): orange, cow, money, freedom. By putting words in sentences, one can express—well, anything that can be expressed in words. The words in sequence can stand for a complicated thought. In the same way that words can represent ideas and things, so can bits. The word and the bit are means by which information is conveyed, though the interpreter must supply the meaning.
>
> **(Lloyd 2006)**

Thus, the information bits may have different meanings and values. In Section 5.2 ("Abstract Complexity Definition"), such bits of information were features, i.e. distinctive substructures (regularities and orderings) of the binary structure (we marked the number of these features with the letter N). The value of these features is equivalent to the complexity of these features (calculated in accordance with the formula for complexity: $(C = N^2/n)$. The value of information determined in this way may serve as a general model of information value. In the above sense, valuable information should also include the so-called free energy:

> The laws of thermodynamics guide the interplay between our two actors, energy and information. To experience another example of the first and second laws, take a bite of an apple. The sugars in the apple contain what is called free energy. Free energy is energy in a highly ordered form associated with a relatively low amount of entropy. In the case of the apple, the energy in sugar is stored not in the random jiggling of atoms but in the ordered chemical bonds that hold sugar together. It takes much less information to describe the form energy takes in a billion ordered chemical bonds than it does

to describe that same energy spread among a billion jiggling atoms. The relatively small amount of information required to describe this energy makes it available for use: that's why it's called free.

(Lloyd 2006)

Therefore, free energy is a "highly ordered form", which is exactly what we have defined as a more complex system/structure. The availability of energy contained in this system is explained by the small amount of information needed to describe it— "the relatively small amount of information required to describe this energy makes it available for use: that's why it's called free". On the one hand, the above conclusion seems logical: less information can be learned more quickly (and therefore easier) than more information. Let's check, however, if this principle is general and consider another example in which the description of energy is also shorter.

If we take, for example, sand or polyethylene instead of sugar, then here we also deal with chemical compounds and not with the accidental movement of atoms, therefore the description of their energy requires less information (it is shorter). According to the above explanation, energy should also be available here for us. However, this does not happen, which contradicts this explanation. The above example shows the application inadequacy of the algorithmic information/complexity outside the technical context, where the information values are various and not determined only by their quantity (as the exemplar is a monkey writing a text more complex than Shakespeare's novel). What is important is the value of information, not the length of its description. Considered an example of apple consumption, in the light of our considerations, it can be interpreted as follows: the availability of (free) energy depends primarily on a sufficiently large number/strength of features (information) common to our body (digestive system) and the product that we want to digest (i.e. a given form of energy which we would like to join) and hence from the possibility of contrast/interaction. The greater the contrast (i.e. a value of the product consumed) the stronger will be the common features of the organism and the product (while maintaining the impact of different characteristics).

Also, the magnitude of contrast of the atomic system and not the length of its description is significant when comparing the set of disordered atoms and the chemical compound. Orderly atoms have more (stronger) characteristics than chaotic ones. Strengthening the impact of common features while maintaining the impact of differentiating features is associated with increased contrast and complexity. Important differentiating features here are isolated (different) atoms that do not cease to be separated after strengthening common features. On the other hand, irrelevant (less distinctive) differences in the random motion of atoms disappear. Thus, chemical compounds are characterized by greater complexity, i.e. higher value of information contained in them than the value (of a larger number) of information contained in disordered atoms.

A similar example was considered in Section 5.2 ("Abstract Complexity Definition"), in which we considered the complexity of the crystal in relation to the disordered state, where the distinguishing atoms were also essential, while we omitted the traits associated with their movement as less important. As we can see, the length of the description (of a system) in both cases is useless.

REFERENCES

Lloyd, S. 2006. *Programming the Universe*. New York: Alfred A. Knopf.
Schroeder, M. 2015. *Spór o pojęcie informacji* [Dispute over the Concept of Information]. Studia Metodologiczne, 34.
Weizsäcker, C.F. 1978. *Jedność Natury* [The Unity of Nature]. Warszawa: PIW, 426–427.

20 Binary Model of Universe

20.1 INTRODUCTION

These considerations about the universe and our presence in it appeared during the search for objective aesthetic criteria (which we have already had the opportunity to familiarize with). Some conclusions from the analysis of various examples of visual interactions were common and required clarification in the form of some general model of such interactions. Following the principle of simplicity and economy of resources, we began the search with a binary structure. It turned out that the sequence of ones and zeros, or white and black squares, can be visually analyzed (for a limited number of elements) similarly as visual structures, and the same general rules governing aesthetic attractiveness apply. First of all, we mean the principle of contrast present in all examples previously analyzed, and the intuitively emerging concept of complexity, which only in the binary structure became clear and definable (as we had the opportunity to find out in Chapter 5, "Contrast as Complexity"). Because never before was the binary structure associated with the area of visual (sensual) and therefore physical interactions, but with abstract structures of mind, the impression of such association was even greater. It showed that the binary structure is the link connecting the world of our thoughts with the physical world. Looking at various binary structures and assessing their visual attractiveness, their (physical) elements, which can be, e.g. squares, ones and stones, do not matter, but the abstract arrangements of these elements, which testifies to the mental nature of these interactions. On the other hand, without physical elements, these interactions (and structures) could not exist.

Awareness of the possibility of combining the material and abstract sphere in the binary structure already went beyond the scope of aesthetic considerations towards epistemology, ontology and metaphysics, for which the binary structure connecting the world of concepts with the physical world was also a common link. It has been assumed that the binary structure can not only model aesthetic interactions, but also the whole of reality. If that were the case, it would be the simplest model of reality/ universe, theoretically possible. Bertalanffy's Theory of Systems provided a strong argument for this possibility:

> According to Bertalanffy: "using Turing Machine which is an abstract machine capable of printing or deleting (1) and (0) signs on an infinitely long tape, it can be demonstrated that it is possible to simulate any process of any complexity provided only that such process can be represented using a finite number of logical operations".
> **(Bertalanffy 1968)**

Although this thesis does not yet identify the binary structure with the universe model, it largely approximates such identification. The discrepancy between the discrete nature of binary structures (in the computational process) and the continuous physical processes that we observe in nature remains to be resolved. However, this difficulty seems to be overcome at a sufficiently fine level of the components of physical objects. Richard Feynman explains:

> The possibility for an accurate simulation to exist, for the computer to do the same as Nature does, requires that everything taking place within a limited space and time be capable of exact analysis using a limited number of logical operations. Currently theories of physics do not satisfy that condition. They treat space as infinitely divisible. On the other hand, the continuity of space and of time is just a postulate. They cannot be proven, since we will be never sure that at some even lower scale, far below our observation capacities, space and time are nevertheless discrete. The connection between natural and computing processes is further strengthened by the quantum theory, which reveals that many physical variables, believed earlier to be continuous, are, in fact, discrete.

> **(Davies 1993)**

Adopting a suitably fine-grained scale solves yet another issue. The simulation consists in the similarity of the computer states to the states of the simulated object. This similarity in typical simulations does not apply directly to binary structures, which in this process only function as codes. However, if we imagine that these object states would be simulated at a level close to the basic level of matter structure, then the structure of the codes would identify with the structure of the object's components.

Binary concepts of universe: the development of digital systems and computer technology in the 1960s and new possibilities associated with it became an inspiration for many theorists such as Carl Friedrich von Weizsäcker, Konrad Zuse, Edward Fredkin, Tom Toffoli, Frank Tipler, David Deutsch, Stephen Wolfram, Seth Lloyd and J. Schmidhuber, for creating concepts and models of the universe. Let's get acquainted with some of them.

- An advanced reality model based on binary archetypal objects was proposed by Weizsäcker in his Theory of Ur-Alternatives (archetypal objects), first publicized in his book *The Unity of Nature* (1980), and further developed through the 1990s. This theory axiomatically constructs quantum physics from the distinction between empirically observable binary alternatives.

     Physicist Holger Lyre in his article *Quantum Theory of Ur-Objects as a Theory of Information* has interpreted Weizsäcker's theory in terms of theory of information. Here information is taken to be the fundamental physical substance, whereas matter and energy are considered to be condensates of information (Lyre 1995).

- Many physicists express the view that physical and computational processes are the same and that theoretically there is a program for a universal computer that processes the dynamic evolution of our world. For example, this computer could be a large cellular automaton. The idea that the universe can be a kind of computer arose in the 1960s:

The connections between computation and physics began to be worked out in the early 1960s by Rolf Landauer at IBM. The idea that computation could take place in a way that respects the underlying information-preserving character of physical law was developed in the 1970s by Charles Bennett at IBM and Edward Fredkin, Tommaso Toffoli, and Norman Margolus at MIT. The idea that the universe might be a kind of computer was proposed in the 1960s by Fredkin and independently by Konrad Zuse, the first person to build a modern electronic computer. Fredkin and Zuse suggested that the universe might be a type of classical computer called a cellular automaton, consisting of a regular array of bits interacting with their neighbours. More recently, Stephen Wolfram has extended and elaborated Fredkin's and Zuse's ideas.

(Lloyd 2006)

The idea of using cellular automata as a basis for a theory of the universe is an appealing one. Let's look at it in more detail:

Konrad Zuse in his book Calculating Space (Zuse 1969), proposed that the physical laws of the universe are fundamentally discrete, and that the entire universe is the output of a deterministic computation on a giant cellular automaton.

Cellular automata (CA) are regular grid of cells, and each cell can be in one of a finite number of states, usually on or/off, or black/white. An initial state of the CA is updated in global discrete time steps, in which each cell's new state changes as a function of its old state and that of a small number of neighbours. A concrete example of Zuse's vision is Conway's Game of Life. The rules are simple: If a cell has 2 black neighbours, it stays the same; if it has 3 black neighbours, it becomes black; otherwise it becomes white. The result is remarkably rich behaviour on the border between randomness and order. A striking feature is the occurrence of gliders, small groups of cells that appear to move like independent emergent entities. It is possible to arrange the automaton so that the gliders interact to perform computations, and it can be shown that the Game of Life is a universal Turing machine (Berlekamp et al. 2001). It is simple to see how this evokes the possibility that we live in a giant CA.

(Markopoulou 2012)

- Another type of computer could also be a universal Turing machine, as suggested by Schmithuber, who showed that there is a very short program that processes all computationally possible universes on an asymptotically optimal way (Schmithuber 1997).
- David Deutsch confirmed that the universe can be thought of as a giant computation as follows:

The laws of physics allow for a machine, the universal Turing machine, such that its possible motions correspond to all possible motions of all possible physical objects. That is, a universal quantum computer can simulate every physical entity and its behaviour. This means that physics, the study of all possible physical systems, is isomorphic to the study of all programs that could run on a universal quantum computer. In short, our universe can be thought of as software running on a universal computer.

(Deutsch 2003)

- Seth Lloyd, initiator of the first quantum computer project, in his book *Programming the Universe* postulates that the universe itself is a giant quantum computer.

  > Every molecule, atom, and elementary particle registers bits of information. Every interaction between those pieces of the universe processes that information by altering those bits. That is, the universe computes, and because the universe is governed by the laws of quantum mechanics, it computes in an intrinsically quantum-mechanical fashion; its bits are quantum bits. The history of the universe is, in effect, a huge and ongoing quantum computation. The universe is a quantum computer.
  >   This begs the question: What does the universe compute? It computes itself. The universe computes its own behaviour. As soon as the universe began, it began computing. At first, the patterns it produced were simple, comprising elementary particles and establishing the fundamental laws of physics. In time, as it processed more and more information, the universe spun out ever more intricate and complex patterns, including galaxies, stars, and planets.

  (Lloyd 2006)

- Stephen Wolfram confirmed that with the help of a computer with adequate computing power, any physical system can be simulated (Wolfram 1985). His book *A New Kind of Science* (Wolfram 2002) presents an empirical study of simple computational systems. Additionally, it argues that for fundamental reasons, these types of systems, rather than traditional mathematics, are needed to model and understand complexity in nature. Wolfram's conclusion is that the universe is digital in its nature and runs on fundamental laws which can be described as simple programs. He predicts that a realization of this within the scientific communities will have a major and revolutionary influence on physics, chemistry and biology and the majority of the scientific areas in general, which is the reason for the book's title.

- The universe with its simulation also identifies the Holographic Principle, formulated in 1993 by a Dutch physicist and Nobel Prize winner Gerard 't Hooft and developed in 1995 by Leonard Susskind (Bousso 2002). It results from quantum statistical thermodynamics and claims that any limited physical object can be equated with a finite amount of information. It is possible to simulate (with binary structures) not only physical processes, but also matter itself. For example, any physical object located in a sphere of 1 sq.m, according to the Holographic Principle, can be equated with information containing no more than 10^{70}bits (Jacyna-Onyszkiewicz 2007).

- Fotini Markopoulou in her paper *The Computing Space-time* (Markopoulou 2012) suggests that the idea the universe is a program in a giant quantum computer can provide a unified picture of physics, and this can be very useful for the problem of Quantum Gravity:

  > Quantum information theory has given a new and interesting twist on the Universe as a Computation. A common idea that is advocated by many practitioners in this field is that everything fundamentally is information, an old idea that can be traced at least back to Wheeler's influential *it from bit*. In that view, all interactions

between physical systems in the universe are instances of information processing, and the information involved in those processes is more primary than the physical systems themselves. Instead of thinking of particles as colliding, we should think of the information content of the particles being involved in a computation. By simple interpolation, the entire universe is nothing but a giant computation. As Lloyd puts it *the universe computes its own dynamical evolution; as the computation proceeds, reality unfolds.*

(Lloyd 2006)

The aforementioned concepts of the universe, based on a binary understanding of reality and information theory, relate indirectly to the conceptual structure of our mind. It can be said that they try to understand the universe from the side of the mind (information), which is different from the physical models of the universe explaining the universe from the material (sensual) side. Although information-based concepts have been around for a long time, they have not yet gained convincing experimental confirmation and are rather treated as unconfirmed intuitions. It seems, however, that this direction of thinking should be given more attention, also to complement/balance the purely physical (material) approach, which, despite a much longer history, has not led to the explanation. Below is a brief, historical overview of these solutions.

20.2   OVERVIEW OF PHYSICAL MODELS OF UNIVERSE

Ancient Greece: for the first Greek philosophers, the world was nature or a place of eternal metabolism. In this way, a physical understanding of being as a material substrate was initiated. The Ionians identified existence with *what is first and basic, of which and what are things*, and which is the potential building block of the entire universe. Tales, as the first of philosophical physicists, pointed to water as the beginning and principle of all things. Others, such as Anaxymenes, pointed to the air, Anaximander to *infinite being*, Heraclitus to fire, Theophrastus to *nature*, Empedocles to *elements* and Anaxagoras to *embryos* or similar particles. All these elements were material and constituted the *arché* of all things.

The Middle Ages: unlike the ancient philosophers who considered the universe to be eternally existing and having no beginning, medieval philosophers considered it to have its origin. It was inspired by the foundations of the Abrahamic religions: Judaism, Christianity and Islam—the creation of the world by God.

Astronomical models: these models of the universe arose simultaneously with the beginnings of astronomy in ancient Sumer. The first models assumed that the world consists of flat land floating in the ocean. This model was later recognized by early Greek philosophers, e.g. Anaximander. Later Greek philosophers, observing the movement of celestial bodies, built models more based on observational facts. The oldest known such model was proposed by Eudoxus of Cnidus. In this model, space and time are infinite, the Earth is spherical and rests in the centre of the universe, and the remaining matter is limited to concentric spheres rotating around it. This model was developed by Aristotle and later refined by Ptolemy. The geocentric model was not the only one recognized by Greeks. According to Archimedes, the heliocentric model was first proposed by Aristarch of Samos (Joshi 2007). In his model, the stars were placed on a sphere with the Sun inside. However, he did not gain broad support among others due to the apparent contradiction with not observing the parallax of the stars (in fact caused by the distance to the stars being much larger than assumed). The only known astronomer who at that time supported the Aristarchal model was Seleukos from Seleucia.

Nicolaus Copernicus: he was the first to use the heliocentric model to develop a simpler way of calculating the position of the planets, which resulted in the gradual acceptance of this model in Western civilization. Copernicus's model assumed that the Earth revolves around its axis, which in time allowed deviation from the concept of heavenly spheres. Thomas Digges corrected this model by stating that the stars are evenly spaced in space. Giordano Bruno further developed this idea, assuming that space is infinite and contains infinitely many stars around which Earth-like planets orbit. This concept was later accepted by scientists such as Isaac Newton and Christiaan Huygens, although it led to several paradoxes. First, it assumed that stars of finite size shine for an infinite time, which means that they produce infinite energy. Secondly, in the infinite universe, the night sky should shine as bright as the surface of the Sun. Thirdly, as Newton noted, an infinite amount of matter in such a space would attract gravity with infinite force, which should immediately collapse.

Theory of relativity: these paradoxes were finally resolved by Albert Einstein's general theory of relativity (1915) and the recognition of the expansion of the universe. All modern models of the universe are built based on this theory. General theory of relativity generalizes special relativity theory and the law of universal gravity, providing a unified description of gravity as the geometric property of time and space, or simply space-time. The space-time curvature is directly related to energy and momentum. Their ratio is specified by the Einstein equation (set of partial differential equations). General relativity allows the creation of many possible models of the universe. Einstein created the first such model (static), assuming that the universe does not change over time. Observations of distant galaxies have shown, however, that the universe is expanding, which has overturned this model. In the following years, two models were taken into account for this expansion: the Big Bang model, in which the universe began its history from one point, and the steady state theory, according to which the expansion of the universe had no beginning, and matter arises in it at a steady pace. The observation of microwave background radiation has refuted the theory of steady state, and the Big Bang model is now considered applicable. It explains the most important observational data: the correlation between distance and redshift of distant galaxies, the same ratio of hydrogen to helium in all areas of the universe and the isotropicity of microwave background radiation.

The Big Bang model: the model assumes that the universe was created as a result of an explosion 13.7 billion years ago from which space, time, matter, energy and interactions emerged. During this expansion, part of the universe's mass had condensed, forming billions of stars. The stars are concentrated in galaxies, of which there are about 10 billion in the part of the universe that we observe. Galaxies cluster into galaxy clusters, which in turn are superclusters, separated from each other by vast expanses of empty space. After a moment of the Big Bang, the universe began to expand. This expansion was due to the force of expansion. Because the force of expansion is counteracted by the force of gravity, there are three possibilities for the later behaviour of the universe. These possibilities were described by Friedman as three models of the universe.

Model 1: the universe is expanding so slowly that gravity is able to slow down and then stop expansion. Then the galaxies begin to approach each other, and the universe is shrinking. Initially, zero distance between galaxies increases to a maximum and then decreases again to zero. There would then be a Great Collapse, which may be followed by another Big Bang. Such a model represents a spatially finished universe—space has no boundaries, but gravity curves it in such a way that it resembles the surface of the Earth.

Model 2: the universe is expanding so fast that gravity cannot stop expansion—it can only slow it down. Initially, the distance is zero, and then the galaxies move apart at a constant speed.

Model 3: the universe is expanding with the minimum speed needed to avoid contraction. Initially, the distance between galaxies is zero, and then it always increases. The speed at which the galaxies recede from each other constantly decreases, but never reaches zero—it asymptotically approaches zero.

The multiverse: the observations of the universe cannot rule out that what we are observing is only one of many disjoint universes that together form the multiverse. Then the word "universe" will not mean everything that exists, but only everything we can observe. From this definition, there is no way to interact with another universe. If such a possibility existed, this other universe would actually be part of ours. Therefore, although science fiction encounters journeys between parallel universes, the word "universe" should not be formally used in such a situation. The concept of a parallel universe assumes that it is physical in the sense that it has its own space-time, its matter and energy and its own set of laws of physics. That is why such a concept should be distinguished from the metaphysical concept of other levels of existence that are not considered physical. Modern science gives at least two possibilities in which many universes can arise. The first is the separation of space-time, which means that no form of matter or energy can get from one area to another. For example, some theories linking cosmological inflation with String Theory allow such phenomena (Linde 1986). The second possibility results from the multi-world interpretation of quantum mechanics. In this interpretation, each quantum measurement causes the universe to divide into as many versions as there are possible results of such measurement. This theme is often used in science fiction. Both of these possibilities, however, are completely speculative and are considered rather unscientific. The fact that parallel universes cannot influence ours in any way means, in particular, that they cannot be experimentally tested, which means that the theory of their existence does not meet the condition of verifiability.

20.3 PHYSICAL AND CONCEPTUAL ANALYSIS

All the above-mentioned attempts to model the universe show a common one-sidedness—they try to explain the universe by analyzing material objects, not taking into account the ability of our mind to detach (abstract) from the properties (of objects) associated with sensual perception, which has evolved through adaptation to specific environmental conditions.

The subject of physics research is phenomena, i.e. the connection of mind structure with the structures of real objects. A phenomenon consists of a common part of an object and the mind and features of mind that a priori take part in the perception. Phenomena can be studied from the side of objects (sensual, material and empirical) or from the mind (abstract, conceptual and a priori). In Chapter 18, "Contrast and Perception of Reality", we have shown how a combination of different visual features may look like on the binary model. On the same model, we will now show the connection of the perceived object and perceiving subject/mind, and how we understand the study of the phenomenon from the side of the object (in its objective part) and from the side of the mind (in its subjective part). Below we see three structures: the object, phenomenon and mind. The phenomenon contains a common part of the object and the mind, and additionally the mind features that a priori take part in the perception (these features correspond to the last three ones in the phenomenon structure). These features arise from the organization of information contained in perceptions.

(object)	1111000011110000111100001010101010
(phenomenon)	10101010111
(subject-mind)	1010101011100111011111011111111111111 ....

If phenomenon can be studied from the side of the object, then it will look like this: 000010101010111; there are additional common features of the phenomenon and the object (represented by four zeros). Such research can be carried out, e.g., by more careful observation. The structure of the mind will also then increase by these common features with the object: 00001010101011100111011111011111111111. One can also study the phenomenon from the side of the mind, that is, analyze those features of the phenomenon that represent the last three ones. During this analysis, there will be new common features of the phenomenon and the mind (represented by two zeros at the end of the phenomenon). The phenomenon will then look like this: 00001010101011100. Studying the phenomenon from the mind side, which would consist in isolating the features of the mind contained in the phenomenon, would, on the one hand, determine what features the object (in itself) does not have and, on the other, better understand how the mind affects observed reality.

Currently, physics investigates phenomena from the material (sensual) side. Although this approach ensures constant contact with the world perceived sensually, and thus empirically verifiable, so far it has not yielded a positive result in explaining the structure of the universe. The reason we see here is the lack of making full use of the mind's ability to think abstractly (which is one of the greatest achievements of evolution), and the failure to take into account the other—*a priori* side (next to the empirical one) of phenomena, i.e. conceptual analysis-introspection of the mind itself. For example, there is a lack of analysis of space as a priori (mental) part of phenomena that Kant first identified (as discussed in Chapter 14, "Contrast as

Cognition"). Physicists use different, theoretical models of space as tools to describe objects/spheres of reality without taking into account its mental aspect. It is enough for them to match the description with observation and experience carried out in specific conditions. Therefore, among others, the laws of quantum mechanics cannot be reconciled with the theory of relativity, because there are different types of space in them. If we took into account the fact that space is a compression of information in our mind and assume that only time really exists—i.e. zero spatial dimension (less convenient, but sufficient to describe reality), then maybe research would also go in a different direction. The higher spatial dimension is also a higher degree of information compression and is associated with the need to organize more information, e.g. to describe our reality (macro-world), we use three-dimensional space and four-dimensional space-time, while in the micro-world (quantum mechanics), where we have a smaller number of information, a flat two-dimensional space is sufficient: "General relativity describes space-time as a manifold M with a dynamical metric field, and gravity as the curvature of that space-time. Quantum field theory describes particle fields on a flat and fixed space-time" (Markopoulou 2012). At an even more basic description of reality, one-dimensional space is sufficient, and at the basic, which is the binary description, the order of changes and their (basic) duration are enough. This is confirmed by the fact that on such a basic, binary level computers can simulate all objects of reality.

In the history of philosophy, little attention has been paid to the mental side of phenomena. Dualists who treat the mind as a different ontological category have partly contributed to this. Nowadays, cognitive science studies the brain rather than the mind. Physicalists, for example, say that there are only objects postulated by physical theories and, as they develop, mental processes will ultimately be explained in terms of these theories. Even if this happened, there would still be no conceptual analysis of mind, to complement the mind-side phenomena, because in this case, physical theories would be based on the components of knowledge to be studied.

A physical approach is effective when it comes to exploring our environment and expanding our knowledge about it, e.g. as in the case of the micro-world. However, if we want to understand the universe, it is necessary to enter an extremely basic level and only from this level begin to build more complex theory. This approach would be an alternative to many unsuccessful attempts to generalize phenomena specific to our environment. The factor increasing this inefficiency is striving to draw general conclusions based on research of hard to reach areas, e.g. the micro-world, where we have limited amount of information and conclusions are often drawn on the basis of incomplete data. Generalizations and theories that are formally very complicated (e.g. String Theory or the concept of quantum universe creation, proposed by Jim Hartley and Steve Hawking in 1983) are formulated, although there is no certainty as to their assumptions, let alone the verifiability of the concepts themselves.

One of the basic concepts of quantum mechanics is the Heisenberg's Uncertainty Principle, concerning the measurement of quantum states, which by many theorists is generalized to the universal law of randomness in the micro-world and even in general. Based on these views, many philosophical concepts (indeterminism and free will) have been created, as well as models of the universe, including multiverse hypothesis. Although this hypothesis has many supporters, even among well-known theorists (David Deutsch) it has no convincing justification, which is characterized below:

> The decoherent-histories picture of quantum mechanics provides an intuitively satisfying resolution to the measurement problem. During measurement, the particle and detector become entangled and the wave function is a superposition of two states. One of these states corresponds to what "actually happens". As long as the future history of particle and detector (...) is decoherent, then the other state has no further effect. The other state—the other part of the wave function—is in some sense still there, however, even though we can safely ignore it. This feature has led some people to advocate the so-called Many Worlds interpretation of quantum mechanics, according to which this other part of the wave function corresponds to another world.
>
> **(Lloyd 2006)**

Since there is not yet a full agreement on an unequivocal understanding of the Uncertainty Principle, attempts to verify it are repeated. These include the research of Cambridge scientists:

> Researchers from the University of Cambridge have taken a peek into the secretive domain of quantum mechanics. In a theoretical paper published in the journal Physical Review A, they have shown that the way that particles interact with their environment can be used to track quantum particles when they're not being observed, which had been thought to be impossible. The founders of modern physics devised formulas to calculate the probabilities of different results from quantum experiments. However, they did not provide any explanations of what a quantum particle is doing when it's not being observed. Earlier experiments have suggested that the particles might do non-classical things when not observed, like existing in two places at the same time. In their paper, the Cambridge researchers considered the fact that any particle travelling through space will interact with its surroundings. These interactions are what they call the "tagging" of the particle. The interactions encode information in the particles that can then be decoded at the end of an experiment, when the particles are measured. The researchers found that this information encoded in the particles is directly related to the wave function that Schrödinger postulated a century ago. Previously the wave function was thought of as an abstract computational tool to predict the outcomes of quantum experiments. "Our result suggests that the wave function is closely related to the actual state of particles", said Arvidsson-Shukur. "So, we have been able to explore the 'forbidden domain' of quantum mechanics: pinning down the path of quantum particles when no one is observing them".
>
> **(Arvidsson-Shukur et al. 2017)**

If these reports were confirmed, it would mean that these theorists were right, who believed that the Uncertainty Principle applies only to the technical (measuring) side of quantum states research and many concepts should be considered erroneous (as in the case of the definition of complexity and the definition of information). It is also worth noting that identifying the abstract wave function of Erwin Schrödinger with the current state of the molecule, which is important here, also confirms the desirability of studying the abstract structure of our mind.

20.4   BINARY MODEL OF REALITY

Conceptual analysis: according to our assumption, when looking for a convincing model of the universe, we should consider and explore both the world external to the mind (physics) and our thinking (introspection), because reality has the features of both. In the history of philosophy, there were examples of such modelling of reality: Heraclitus was the first philosopher to speak of reason operating in the universe: *reason is not specifically human, but cosmic force, man only participates in it*; Hegel believed that *a component of being is the same as a component of logical thought, i.e. the concept* (Tatarkiewicz 1981). However, this approach is missing in modern physics, dominated by the positivist understanding of science. Since the mind belongs to reality, it can be assumed that the creation of its structures from simple to more complex should be similar to the organization of reality structures (external to the mind).

Physics seeks to uncover the basic physical component of the universe and the way in which it produces complex structures. Therefore, if we succeed in isolating the simplest (basic) component of our mind and thus in building a general model for generating structures out of these components, such a model should correspond (by analogy) to the creation of structures present in physical reality. Let us try and challenge the above hypothesis by assuming that, as a result of physical investigations, we have discovered the most basic element for which the corresponding component of our mind is not the most simple (basic) but complex. In such an eventuality, our mind would not be able to accept it as the basic (simplest) physical component because any additional feature (i.e. bit of information) would require an additional quantum of energy, both in the mind and in reality (as the theory of information tells us), whereas we are looking for the smallest possible amount (quantum) of energy. It follows that the simplest component of the mind must correspond to the simplest physical component.

The components of our mind are concepts. The simplest component of the mind is the notion of "one", since it has only one feature. All other concepts of our mind show greater complexity, and it can be assumed that by breaking them down into ever simpler elements we will eventually reach "one". In contrast, "one" as the most basic concept cannot be analyzed further and represents the limit to our exploration/understanding. Likewise, in physics, the inquiry must stop at the basic quantum of energy.

What is the correspondence between the mental quantum and the physical quantum? It can be assumed that "one" is the mental (abstract) model for the basic quantum of energy. That abstract model in our mind is nothing more than an electric impulse equipped with appropriate energy (higher than that of the basic quantum in physics).

As discussed before (this was discussed in the Chapter 17, "Contrast as Being"), we also need to accept the lack of one, or zero, as the basic component of the universe/being:

> The basic being, i.e. the contrast between one and zero (which as the simplest is the limit of inquiry for our mind) can be considered self-existent and necessary because

just as there is no one without zero, so there is no zero without one (they cannot be separately distinguished). In other words, there must be something that "exists", so that nothing "exists", (if there wasn't something, it wouldn't be known that something was missing) and vice versa—something must be missing to notice its existence.

It is worth realizing this limitation because it is also a limitation for inquiries in physics, which are closely related to our mind. Currently, physics does not take it into account when only one-sidedly exploring the "material" side of reality ("material" in quotation marks because our mind is also material, which has been discussed in the Chapter 15, "Mind-Body Problem"). New particles are being discovered; more and more complicated theories are being created, which (one has to agree with it) can never be fully verified unless we specify what verification is itself and what limits it.

With one and zero as the basic components, one should define the way they build reality. By joining this task, we should realize that if we consider the universe at a basic level, we also have the resources available at this level, i.e. basic energy quanta and elementary concepts related to their organization. They must be enough to create the structures of the universe. No laws of physics and no complex theoretical concepts apply here because they are not possible at this level.

With the quantum of mind (one), we can go down to the basic level and consider how to create complex structures of these quanta. It should correspond to the real formation of structures. The easiest way to create structures from basic energy quanta (both mental and real) is to replace ones with these quanta in an abstract (zero-one) binary string. To be treated as a model of reality, it would have to meet at least two conditions:

1. It should contain in itself all possible structures of the universe and thus all the corresponding combinations of zeros and ones.
2. It should change over time.

After analyzing different possibilities (which included various types of binary structures, algorithms and computer programs), guided by simplicity, we come to the conclusion that a structure containing all other structures (combinations of zeros and ones) and changing over time is *an infinitely long, constantly increasing binary number*. Its increase (which we also determine according to the principle of simplicity) occurs in the smallest (basic) time interval by the basic (smallest) value, i.e. by one. Below are the initial values of such a growing number (from 1 to 33).

1, 10, 11, 100, 101, 110, 111, 1000, 1001, 1010, 1011, 1100, 1101, 1110, 1111, 10000, 10001, 10010, 10011, 10100, 10101, 10110, 10111, 11000, 11001, 11010, 11011, 11100, 11101, 11110, 11111, 100000, 100001, ...

Why does this number contain all possible combinations/structures? It is easy to see that all binary numbers with a given total number of zeros and ones (n) are a set of all possible combinations of these zeros and ones. For example, all binary three-element numbers: 100, 101, 110, 111, 011, 010, 001, 000 exhaust all possible combinations of zeros and ones.

Analogies to reality: the sequence of ones and zeros is difficult to relate to reality directly, because its level is too abstract. What's interesting, in this simple binary number, is one can find many analogies with reality. Let's list some of them:

1. "One" can be treated as the basic, smallest and indivisible component (energy quantum) of reality, while "zero" as its absence.

2. The time of binary number increase by (one) can be taken as the basic (shortest) time of changes in reality. It would also be the duration of the basic impulse (one) and the duration of the shortest interval between impulses (zero).

3. The steady increase in binary number is analogous to the observed expansion of the universe.

4. The presence of ones and zeros may indicate the presence of symmetry in the universe.

5. The cyclical nature of changes and repetitions in binary structure resembles the cyclical nature of natural phenomena. It can also be seen that the structures of zeros and ones within consecutive numbers are changing. These changes occur at different speeds depending on the size of the number and the location of these structures in it. Example: 1000001, 1000010, 1000011, 1000100, ..., 1010000, 1010001, ..., 1100000, 1100001, 1100010, 1100011, 1100100, 1100101, ...

   We see that the fastest changes occur at the end of the number and the slowest at the beginning.

6. When we look at binary numbers with the same total number of zeros and ones (n), in sequence (from smallest to largest), we notice that at the beginning, their complexity is close to zero (zeros dominate), then it increases, stays and decreases again at the end to zero (ones dominate). It is similar to the emergence and disappearance (disintegration) of complex objects in reality (including a human). Example: 1000000000, ..., 1011011100, ..., 1111111111. Here we see three ten-element numbers: the first—with minimal complexity, the intermediate—with greater complexity and the last—again with minimal complexity.

7. The ability to create arbitrarily complex binary structures (according to the proposed definition of complexity—ACD) allows the representation of any real objects/structures by binary structures.

8. An increase in the binary number may indicate the increase in energy in the universe associated with its expansion.

9. Determination of changes in binary number may be associated with irreversibility of thermodynamic processes. It may also indicate a lack of causality.

10. The presence of (only) ones in each largest number with a given number n (example in item 5) may also indicate condensed energy, e.g. in black holes. However, the transition from the ones to the next number (one and only zeros), which may correspond to a white hole, can be associated with (larger and smaller) explosions and their cyclicality. The presence of longer

sequences of ones in intermediate numbers can be an analogy to the black holes observed in the universe.

11. In Chapter 16, "Artificial Intelligence, Self-Awareness and Creativity", we have presented the record of music in the form of a binary structure in an analogous manner, i.e. one, where the binary structure is not a conventional code but is identified with music. Because music is an important component of reality, its identification with the binary structure confirms the reality of the binary structure and the truth of the proposed concept of the universe. The direct relationship of the universe with music and numbers was also the basis of the Pythagorean theory of being (which was discussed in Chapter 17, "Contrast as a Being"). There, however, intuitions were much more general. In our concept, the universe can even be identified with music, because music, as we have previously shown, can be identified with a binary structure.

We can notice that even with such a cursory assessment, the similarity of a simple binary number to reality structures seems surprising.

Understanding space: in our earlier considerations (Chapter 18, "Contrast and Perception of Reality"), we noticed the difficulty of direct transition from the abstract level (binary model) to reality and introduced an indirect visual model to facilitate such a transition. There, we tried to draw attention to the analogies of binary structures and structures of real objects perceived sensually. Let's try to imagine our model, which is a growing binary number, at the most basic level. As the binary number increases, it creates successive binary numbers that identify with subsequent states of the universe. Example: ..., 1000, 1001, 1010, 1011, 1100, ... These subsequent numbers as successive states of the universe appear at intervals that can be equated (let's assume) with the basic (Planck) time intervals. At this level, we have no spatial dimensions, only time (defined as zero spatial dimension), which is why we can only speak of the sequence of numbers/states. Each such state, e.g. 1011, has its structure of ones and zeros, which also occur in some order. Perception or remembering these different types of order would be very uncomfortable for our minds. That is why other types/ways of perceiving (recording, imagining) the order have emerged, i.e. spatial dimensions. We witnessed a similar process during the evolution of information recording from perforated and magnetic tapes to discs and memory cards (in the future also spatial media are envisaged). Thanks to this, we do not have to perceive structure 1011 in sequence, i.e. first 1, then 0, then 1, then 1, but we see the whole structure "simultaneously" ("simultaneously" in quotation marks, because in reality we also see these digits in some order, but we have direct access to them, which facilitates their organization and accelerates perception). Hence the sense of simultaneity, which we also have, e.g., looking at an image. In fact, we also perceive image elements in order. The higher the spatial dimension, the more effective is the organization (which can also be understood as information compression); it enables the organization of more information at the same time or less, with less energy expenditure.

To better understand this process, imagine a thousand balls with a diameter of 1 cm, located side by side in a straight line (one ball symbolizes one information).

The length of this straight section of balls will be 10 m. The same balls can be placed in a square with a side of (approximately) 32 cm, or in a cube with a side of 10 cm. We can see here that a higher spatial dimension can be associated with easier and faster access to the same or more information, which is also associated with better organization (compression) of information and energy saving. In physics, in addition to space perceived with senses (i.e. three-dimensional), other types of space are also used to describe reality, which should be understood as formal models that simplify the description (compressing information in our mind). These include multidimensional spaces, including four-dimensional (Minkowski) space, Hilbert space and Banach space.

To illustrate the aforementioned states of the universe, we will use two-dimensional space, i.e. the plane of this page. We will place vertically the next states of the universe. On the other hand, the horizontal order of digits means successive elements of the structure of a given state of the universe.

1000
1001
1010
1011
1100

By using the second spatial dimension instead of the zero dimension (time), we do not have to remember all the ordering here, which is a great help in processing more information.

Note: the above conclusions regarding the spatial dimensions were formulated mainly on the basis of visual structure analysis and introspection. They show that space is a product of our mind and not a property of the outside world. This view is shared by some philosophers (e.g. Kant), others believe that space is an independent entity or relationship between entities.

In these considerations, we treat space, like mathematics, as an interpretation of reality, with the difference that we have been equipped with "spatial interpretation" by evolution (we do not have to learn it). We treat space as a compression of information in our mind, which takes certain forms (spatial), consciously felt as characteristic qualities (we previously defined such qualities as qualia, i.e. the most complex, emergent structures of consciousness).

Standard Questions

Every concept of the universe, including this one, requires answers to standard questions:

1. Did the universe have a beginning and a cause?
2. Is it finished?
3. What empirical verification capabilities does it have?
4. What are the relationships of this model with other models of the universe?

Answer 1: from our considerations, it follows that the reason for the existence of the universe is a logical necessity resulting from the impossibility of existence of "zero" state (nothingness) without the "one" state (different from nothingness) and vice versa. It is worth realizing that this logical necessity results directly from the limitation of our mind, which means that apart from being and nothingness, "coupled" with each other, we have no other choice. Logically, we cannot accept only emptiness (without being) and only being (without emptiness). It is particularly difficult to imagine the lack of possibility (of existence) of the void itself—after all, the state of zero seems conceivable. Paradoxically, this possibility results from the fact that emptiness can only be found by something different from emptiness, i.e. our mind (being and one). Emptiness defines being (something that exists) and vice versa—being defines emptiness. Emptiness in isolation from being is impossible—if there were no being, there would be no emptiness. The question arises, what would it be then, i.e. if there was neither emptiness nor being? We don't know the answer to this question, and we will never be able to answer, because the answer would go beyond the limits of our mind. In this way, the above-mentioned logical necessity should be understood. A similar idea of being existed in various forms in the history of philosophical thought, e.g. in Chinese Buddhism (Yin-Yang doctrine), in the philosophy of Plato, who claimed that existence is a game of being with non-being, or Hegel, who identified existence with nothingness.

It remains an open question whether this logical necessity, which is atemporal (independent of time), from which it follows that the universe has always existed and had no beginning, should be treated only as the limit of our mind or whether it also constitutes an objective law (of nature) that also functions outside our mind. The answer to this question is associated with the adoption of one of three possible interpretations of the universe model, which include: (1) the pantheistic model, i.e. one in which God identifies with the universe—then the border of our thinking would coincide with the borders of the universe; (2) panentheistic model, one in which the universe is a part of God—then God would not be knowable by us in the part outside the universe (i.e. outside our minds); (3) atheistic model, i.e. one in which there is no God and the universe is self-existent—then the boundaries of the universe would coincide with the boundaries of our mind, as in the pantheistic model. The idea of a self-existent universe also functions as a physical concept. This is called a model of quantum creation of the universe from nothingness proposed by Jim Hartley and Steve Hawking (Hartle and Hawking 1983). This model is based on the idea of the universe emergence from fluctuations of the quantum vacuum, which ten years earlier was proposed by Edward Tryon (Tryon 1973), and combines two models of gravity quantization: a model using the concept of the quantum wave function of the universe and a model of the so-called path integral. The essence of this conception is the assumption that at the quantum level, because of the Uncertainty Principle, the law of conservation of energy can be broken for just a brief moment, causing virtual particles to pop in and out of existence. Virtual particles could also have existed in the vacuum that was here before our universe existed, and these quantum fluctuations from nothing (the vacuum) eventually led to one of these particles popping into existence and becoming our universe. According to our model, the universe had no beginning, and emptiness (vacuum) is impossible without something that states it. In this sense, it doesn't make sense to emerge from nothingness. However, it would be possible to emerge something but not from metaphysical nothingness in which no laws of physics (quantum and relativistic) can exist, but from the so-called quantum vacuum, which is not absolute nothingness. Such creation of the universe should also be understood not in an absolute but in a local way. It could correspond with our model (*increasing binary number*) at times when this number increases the amount of digits by one, i.e. when going from ones (only) to one with zeros (only).

Answer 2: the binary number increases without interruption, increasing its size by one in the basic, shortest possible time in nature (Planck interval). This steady increase can be explained by counting/cumulating one and zero states that alternate (since none of them are independent, as has already been discussed). An increasing binary number is the only counting method possible at the basic level because it only uses the concepts available at this level, i.e. the amount and size of digits (one is greater than zero) and their order. One can speculate how and why such counting is carried out and we are not dealing, for example, with the simple order of zeros and ones (10101010 …)?—For now, we give up these considerations. We assume that this number increases to infinity, because it has always been growing (such a necessity has always existed), thus its beginning also lies in infinity. Knowing the relationship that exists between the amount of zeros and ones (n) of a binary number and the amount of possible values of this number (i.e. the amount of combinations of zeros and ones) which is ($x = 2^n$), we can calculate the growth rate of the binary number when the amount of these combinations strives for infinity. We have the relationship: $n = \log x$, the growth rate (v) will be a derivative of this function (assuming that it is approximately continuous) $v = n' = 1/x\ln2$; when x goes to infinity, v goes to zero. Thus, we see that the growth rate (and therefore increase) of the binary number tends to zero, despite the fact that changes within this number occur at a constant rate (increase of binary number by one, in Planck time). There is some analogy here with Friedman's third model (above), in which the speed at which galaxies move away from each other constantly decreases, but never reaches zero—it asymptotically approaches zero.

Answer 3: to confirm empirically the proposed hypothesis, one should find a transition between the abstract binary structure and material reality. This could be done by assigning energy to ones in a sequence of ones and zeros. We realize that we have to deal with such materialized binary structures on a daily basis and they are digital signals used for data transmission, e.g. in telecommunications. Although the binary structures appearing in them are not autonomous (performing only the role of information codes), the presence of such structures in reality and close proximity significantly approximates the sought confirmation. Electromagnetic waves have energy, but they cannot be treated as material objects. However, we know that it is possible to convert energy into matter. The question then arises whether and eventually how it would be possible to convert such waves into material objects. Here, the de Broglie hypothesis comes to the aid, which says that all material objects have a corpuscular-wave character, i.e. they are also waves (of matter). Having the above theoretical premises, one can think about experimental confirmation.

In our experiment, we would like to transform a binary wave into a material object. How would such a wave differ from the mentioned digital signals?—In that it should have, in addition to properly selected standard parameters, such as frequency and amplitude, also an appropriate complexity that would correspond to the complexity of the (represented) material object. The experiment could consist in emitting a binary structure (e.g. 111001010000110 …) in the form of a series of pulses (e.g. from a laser) and observing it for the presence of material particles. Such a sequence of pulses corresponds to (is equivalent) a wave packet (several overlapping sine waves). Wave packets as energy condensates can correspond to material objects. Until now, the complexity of such wave packets is not taken into account in quantum mechanics, probably because it would be very difficult for sine waves and because the definition of the complexity of the binary structure is not widespread yet. The emission of the packet of sine waves in binary form (e.g. a sequence of laser pulses) would allow the introduction of complexity into the wave packet, and thus to the corresponding material object, if any. Currently, physics does not take into account and does not examine the possibility of binary recording of the structures of matter or the complexity of matter, although material objects are complex. The proposed model enabling analysis of reality from the side of abstract binary structures allows both to take into account the complexity of material objects and to record their structure. This direction is proposed as an alternative to the search for solutions that are closely related to the existing physical description.

Current academic textbook examples of de Broglie waves do not take into account the complexity of material objects by assigning to each of them one wave of unchanging length/frequency, i.e. a wave of virtually zero complexity. Below is an example of attributing the de Broglie wave to a man, an electron and a football.

Macroscopic objects can also be treated as a wave of matter, but the length of such a wave is so short that it becomes unmeasurable. It is said that macroscopic objects do not reveal their wave properties. For example, it can be calculated that for a man weighing 50 kg moving at a speed of 10 km/h, the wavelength of matter is: $\lambda = 4.77 \times 10^{-36}$ m. This value is so small that it is impossible to detect human wave properties.

(https://pl.wikipedia.org/wiki/Fale_materii)

Another academic example calculates the de Broglie wavelength for an electron: $\lambda = 0.73 \times 10^{-9}$ m. and for a ball: $\lambda = 6.63 \times 10^{-35}$ m. One can see that the length of the electron-associated wave of matter is much greater than the wavelength of the ball. Therefore, wave properties are revealed only in the case of micro-world objects.

The above example shows that the energies of electromagnetic waves would have to be very large here: the larger the energies the shorter the wavelengths. This involves technical difficulties in emitting short enough high-frequency pulses from the laser. Currently, femtosecond pulses are possible ($1fs = 10^{-15}s$) while the Planck time is 5.39×10^{-44}. It follows that in the proposed experiment, the possible particles of matter would differ in "granularity" from existing particles (created "naturally" by basic impulses), because the smallest impulses available are not basic impulses. There would, however, be a full analogy of creating their structures.

To increase the likelihood of creating a material object (suppose it would be a particle at this stage), the impulses should have high energy and be very close to each other (temporally and spatially). However, this is only one condition. The second condition is the right order of zeros and ones, which contains information about the object-particle structure and its complexity. There can be many ideas for such an experiment. For example, to get more condensation, one could focus the rays from different sides at one point, taking care of their order.

Answer 4: the proposed Binary Model of the Universe is among the concepts that place the main emphasis on the informational side of reality. The inspiration for these concepts was the development of information theory and related technology, in particular, the theoretical possibility of computer simulation of all physical objects and processes. Konrad Zuse and Edward Fredkin were pioneers here, who also proposed the idea of the universe as a universal, digital computer:

> The idea that the universe might be, at bottom, a digital computer is decades old. In the 1960s, Edward Fredkin, then a professor at MIT, and Konrad Zuse, who constructed the first electronic digital computers in Germany in the early 1940s, both proposed that the universe was fundamentally a universal digital computer. More recently, this idea has found an advocate in the computer scientist Stephen Wolfram.
>
> **(Lloyd 2006)**

This concept was made even more real by the quantum computer project (initiated by Seth Lloyd), in which physical processes are identified with computational ones. Lloyd writes in more detail about this relationship in his book *Programming the Universe*:

> In brief, the simulation proceeds as follows: First, map the state of every piece of a quantum system—every atom, electron, or photon—onto the state of some small set of quantum bits, known as a quantum register. Because the register is itself quantum-mechanical, it has no problem storing the quantum information inherent in the original system on just a few quantum bits. Then enact the natural dynamics of the quantum system using simple quantum logic operations—interactions between quantum bits. Because the dynamics of physical systems consists of interactions between its constituent parts, these interactions can be simulated directly by quantum logic operations mapped onto the bits in the quantum register that correspond to those parts.
>
> This method of quantum simulation is direct and efficient. The amount of time the quantum computer takes to perform the simulation is proportional to the time over which the simulated system evolves, and the amount of memory space required for the simulation is proportional to the number of subsystems or sub-volumes of the simulated system. The simulation proceeds by a direct mapping of the dynamics of the system onto the dynamics of the quantum computer. Indeed, an observer that interacted with the quantum computer via a suitable interface would be unable to tell the difference between the quantum computer and the system itself. All measurements made on the computer would yield exactly the same results as the analogous measurements made on the system.
>
> **(Lloyd 2006)**

The concept of universe as a quantum computer (UCC) is much in line with our concept of the universe as a growing binary number (UBN). First of all, for both concepts, the basis is a binary structure of reality/universe in which the basic components identify with single bits of information. In the case of UCC, these basic components are elementary particles (as the simplest currently known components of the universe); in UBN, they are the simplest theoretically possible components (i.e. ones and zeros). The growing binary number, like the UCC, is conceivable as the output of a computer, generated by a simple program. At UCC, this program is created accidentally as a result of quantum fluctuations:

> Computers are simple machines. They operate by performing a small set of almost trivial operations, over and over again. But despite their simplicity, they can be programmed to produce patterns of any desired complexity, and the programs that produce these patterns need not possess any apparent order themselves: they can be random sequences of bits. The generation of random bits does play a key role in the establishment of order in the universe, just not as directly as Boltzmann imagined.
>
> The universe contains random bits whose origins can be traced back to quantum fluctuations in the wake of the Big Bang. We have seen how these random bits can serve as "seeds" of future detail ranging from the positions of galaxies to the locations of mutations in DNA. These random bits, introduced by quantum mechanics, in effect programmed the later behaviour of the universe.
>
> **(Lloyd 2006)**

In UBN, it would be a program that generates a growing binary number, i.e. all possible binary structures. The UCC model does not specify (even hypothetically) the interactions resulting in the formation of elementary particles and their features (states), which are treated here as basic. UBN, on the other hand, identifies all interactions with basic (smallest) energy pulses of different frequency (according to the structure of the binary number). It also assumes that at the basic level, neither the quantum computer nor its program nor the laws of quantum mechanics are conceivable, because at this level, there are no such complex concepts. For the description of the universe at this basic level, much simpler concepts are sufficient, which include: the one, zero, their order (structure) and the shortest (basic) time interval. Despite these differences, both concepts are based on a binary understanding of reality and indicate, although in a different way, the relationships (and even identity) between "binarity notion" and physical processes and objects. It is particularly interesting that these concepts derive from completely different areas of our knowledge, i.e. from information theory and aesthetics.

Another model of universe that combines the concepts of binarity and information with physics is the theory of Ur-Objects ("ur" in German means "pre") by Weizsäcker, based on a philosophical analysis, equating energy with information. The universe is made up of components (ur-objects) that are at the same time the basic quantum of matter and information. The principle of creating events and objects is based here on resolving of simple alternatives (pre-alternatives), which Weizsäcker explains as follows:

Information contained in an event can also be defined as the number of unresolved simple alternatives that are resolved when the event occurs. A simple alternative should be considered as unresolved in such a way that neither of its two answers is more likely than the other. As a measure of the multitude of forms of an object, we can now take the number of simple alternatives that must be resolved to describe the form of that object. In this sense, the information "contained" in an object is the information entitled to the event of occurrence of this object as identified by observer in the field of view.

Matter is a form. We know matter today as elementary particles. They should be constructed with the pre-alternatives. Pre-alternatives are the ultimate elements of possible forms; resolved pre-alternatives are the ultimate elements of real forms.

Mass is information. Approximately not taking into account forces (I can't cope with the theory of interactions) the information of a certain situation is simply the number of its pre-alternatives. According to the simplest model of a particle with mass, its resting mass is the number of pre-alternatives necessary to build a particle at rest, and thus equals exactly the information invested in the particle.

Energy is information. Relativistic equating of mass with energy allows to transfer to energy everything that has been said about mass. In the case of kinetic energy, relations are even formally the simplest. A free pre-object has constant energy, the smallest quantum of energy E_0 possible in cosmos.

(Weizsäcker 1980)

Similarly to the UCC concept, physical objects and processes are identified here with information processing (resolving simple alternatives). Both concepts are derived from (probability-based) laws of quantum mechanics. This could indicate that both complexity and causality in the universe arose completely by accident. Such randomness results (implicitly) from Weizsäcker's theory. It is different in the case of the UCC concept, in which Lloyd notices that something else means randomness when, e.g., monkeys write text on a typewriter, and otherwise if the same monkeys would write such random text on the computer keyboard as its program, then it would be much easier with interesting results:

What happens when the computer tries to execute this random program? Most of the time, it will become confused and stop, issuing an error message. Garbage in, garbage out. But some short computer programs—and thus, programs with a relatively high probability of being randomly generated—actually have interesting outputs. For example, a few lines of code will make the computer start outputting all the digits of pi (π). Another short program will make the computer produce intricate fractals. Another short program will cause it to simulate the standard model of elementary particles. Another will make it simulate the early moments of the Big Bang. Yet another will allow the computer to simulate chemistry. And still another will start the computer off toward proving all possible mathematical theorems.

(Lloyd 2006)

This concept is similar to UBN because such a short program can also generate subsequent binary numbers from zero to infinity. However, obtaining these numbers by accidentally pressing the keys on a typewriter is theoretically and practically impossible.

The difference between Lloyd's and Weizsäcker's concepts also lies in the adoption of other basic components of the universe. In the case of UCC, these are elementary particles, while in Weizsäcker's theory, they are pre-objects, i.e. the smallest energy quantum (E_0) possible in cosmos, of which also elementary particles are composed. This is the simplest level theoretically possible. We also deal with a similar basic level in the UBN concept.

The proposed Binary Model of Universe, in contrast to existing solutions, takes into account the complexity of objects/structures using the structural definition of information and the associated Abstract Complexity Definition. The applications of these definitions are shown in many examples present in this work. The binary model was created as a natural consequence of earlier aesthetic and epistemological investigation. We treat it as a hypothesis, but special among the existing ones, because it is the simplest of theoretically possible. Despite this simplicity, due to the association of binary structure, successively with aesthetics, complexity, energy and de Broglie waves, there is also a combination of philosophical and physical areas, which complement each other. There is also suggested a possibility of experimental way to confirm this hypothesis.

20.5 BASIC CONCEPTS

Using the above outlined binary model of reality, we will now make a tentative attempt to define the most fundamental concepts, associated with this model.

Basic quantum of energy: the simplest, indivisible, distinguishable element having only one feature, that of being able to separate itself. This would be the prime or first matter (prote hyle), which was described by Aristotle as unknowable due to its lacking any form (the form being the source of knowledge). At this point, it should be observed that, while the binary structure (composed of basic quanta, i.e. ones, and their absence, i.e. zeros) can be infinitely complex, it also marks the limit of our understanding, given that "one" is the most basic element of our mind, too. It follows that we will never be able to understand the origin of the basic impulse. We can only try to understand the structure of the universe based on its existence. The realization of that constraint should be regarded as equivalent to the explanation.

The basic time interval: this is the duration of the shortest change—the shortest, basic interval serving as a measure of time. This can be the duration of the basic impulse (one) or the interval between impulses (zeros). It is also the time of the binary number which increases by the smallest value, i.e. by one. It can be assumed that this basic interval is equal to Planck's time, that is, 5.39×10^{-44}s, or smaller.

Matter, mass and energy: the aggregate quantity of basic quanta of energy (ones).

Material objects: structures with sufficiently large energy (with greater or smaller complexity) to be perceived sensually.

Abstract objects: thoughts and structures with relatively little energy (greater or smaller) "perceived" and processed by the mind.

Structure: an object/structure of our mind, the designation of the word "structure", the common feature of all complex objects, which signifies an arrangement of elements of such objects. Let us consider how this abstract notion is produced in our mind. We note (a thought appears) that elements of a complex object are arranged in some order. At the instance when this "observation" is made, there appears in our mind an (electrochemical) impulse, which is perceived/experienced as precisely that thought. Next, we notice that elements of other complex objects are also arranged in some manner, which is a feature the objects hold in common. Once again, an impulse is generated corresponding to that common feature. Subsequently we assign the name "structure" to it, which means that a new impulse is created, associated with the word "structure" and with that impulse being the common feature here. The activation of any of these impulses causes the other impulses to be activated.

Interaction/impact (contrast): a tension between the effects of common and differing features. The greater the interaction the more/stronger the common and differing features have contrasting objects. This is the most general (abstract) understanding of impact/interaction in both a philosophical and a physical sense. At this general level, the definition brings a new essential quality: "tension" that has not been considered so far (in the context of interaction) and which is crucial here. At this general level, it is also possible to distinguish tension components which are common and differing features. These notions allow a quantitative analysis of the impact at every level of generality, from extremely abstract (binary structure) to specific material objects (more information can be found in Chapters 3 and 6).

Being: contrast, tension, impact and interaction (more information can be found in Chapter 17).

Force (physical or material contrast): the force increases when common and differentiating features have greater energy (ones are more numerous).

Space: in interpreting reality as a constantly increasing binary number, we followed the principle of parsimony, that is, we strove to reduce as far as possible the number of concepts required to construct this model. The necessary concepts are as follows: basic impulse (one) and absence of impulse (zero) or the shortest distance in time between impulses (basic time interval). All other concepts may be defined using the above notions, including the concept of space. The increasing binary number is composed of elements (impulses and time intervals) that follow each other in a specific order. Such number is characterized only by a temporal dimension. The mind finds it difficult to grasp, because in order to do so, we would have to memorize the sequence of all the elements and access each of them in the proper order, as in the case of a tape recording. This explains why our mind generates a spatial-linear dimension which makes it easier for the mind to access all elements of the number. The same applies to the second and third dimensions that facilitate our perception of more complex reality. The addition of further dimensions by our mind relates to the increase in the number of information items used by us and the need to compress them. Three-dimensional space (spatial vision) represents precisely such compression (organization) of information. Information compression consists in the recording of a specific number of information items using fewer bits, i.e. less energy. From this definition, it follows that space should be treated as a non-physical but mental category (which does not prevent physicists to use it in physics). Similarly, the binary structure and the present (conceptual) considerations as well could also be incorporated into physical research, thereby obtaining a higher integration level of physics with philosophy.

Form: considered at the basic level, it is a binary structure or an arrangement of zeros and ones. It contains the entire information about the structure. Just as no form/structure exists by itself in reality, the notion of structure must have its energy-based equivalent in our mind (electrochemical impulses).

Information: each substructure (an emerging arrangement) of zeros and ones in the binary structure. This could be considered as the most abstract, general and simplest (archetypical) understanding of information (which is also sometimes defined as structural information) because it refers to the binary model. All other definitions of information suffer from having practical connotations. The most commonly accepted definition, since it was adopted for telecommunication's purposes (coding), was proposed by Shannon. According to that definition, a binary communication composed of (n) zeros and ones contains a quantity of information equal to the number of all combinations of zeros and ones in (n) elements or 2^n. That number is equal to the inverse of the probability of selecting the correct combination, that is, the uncertainty which is eliminated when such selection is made. In this case, information is transmitted in the form of a communication and (in contrast to the abstract definition formulated earlier) it is not intrinsic to the communication itself, but is a function of the set (catalogue) from which the communication in question originates. This conception, in its practical sense is artificial and says nothing about the message itself (more information can be found in Chapter 19).

Complexity (in abstract sense): means complexity (C) of the binary structure. It is equal to the product of the degree of complexity (D) and the number of substructures (N). The degree of complexity is the ratio of the number of substructures (features and information items) and the number of basic elements (n) or zeros and ones (D = N/n). It denotes information compression (parsimony and message conciseness), without taking into account the total quantity of information included in the structure. Intuition tells us, however, that the larger the amount of information, the harder it is to compress/organize it. To allow for this condition, we multiply the degree of complexity (D) by the number of substructures (N). In this manner, we obtain the definition of complexity as the ratio of the square number of substructures and the number of basic elements ($C = N^2/n$). This is the so-called Abstract Complexity Definition (Stanowski 2011). It can be identified with (mental) contrast (more information can be found in Chapter 5).

Compression of information: means either decreasing the number of basic elements (zeros and ones) while keeping the number of substructures (regularities) constant or increasing the number of substructures with the number of basic elements remaining the same. It can be identified with increasing the degree of complexity (D) or organization. We know from information theory that transmitting, receiving and storing information requires energy. Compression (consisting in improved organization) makes it possible to save energy, since the same number of zeros and ones now contains a greater amount of information (number of substructures). The ones are just portions of energy. Additional substructures (patterns) created as a result of such compression do not require energy. They can be described as pure form (so greatly appreciated by artists). Nevertheless, they are not self-contained, because they can be only a result of organizing the elements equipped with energy. They depend on the latter since in the absence of those elements (and hence without their energy), there will be nothing to arrange. This explains the contentious issue of the relationship between information and energy (more information can be found in Chapter 6).

Human being: the binary structure of reality of high complexity.

Mind: the binary structure of the greatest complexity (known to us) having the most common features with human.

Perception: just like the perceived object, the perceiving subject (human being) is the structure of information. Perception should be understood more generally as the linking of our structure with the structure of the object. The linking of different (i.e. having differentiating features) structures is the contrast between these structures and hence development (growth) (more information can be found in Chapter 14).

Cognition: the appropriation by the subject of the object's differentiating features through the features the subject and the object have in common. The object may be material or mental. In either case, we are dealing here with contrast subject-object.

20.6 SUMMARY

The association of a binary number with reality did not occur immediately and was a result of an attempt to capture in a concise form the essence of visual interactions, as well as (after generalization) interactions in general. Binary structures have been used here as models of objects and their interactions. The *Binary Model of Universe* is therefore a consequence of analogies between these structures and phenomena directly observed in reality. Ontological considerations occur when abstract binary structures become almost perceived sensually, in a sense they "connected mind with body". The search in this direction was intensified after becoming familiar with the existing concepts of the universe derived from the theory of digital systems (the universe as a computer, computer program, cellular automaton, etc.).

When constructing the model, we tried to follow the principle of simplicity and parsimony, i.e. using a minimum amount of means: if something (some content) could be expressed using two terms, we do not use three, let alone more. So it's also a way to compress information. Thanks to this method, the proposed *Binary Model of Universe* is extremely simple. This simplicity (of ordinary binary number), in combination with the huge complexity of reality, seems difficult to accept. It is difficult to accept that contrasts (interactions), beauty, being, our feelings, as well as all the explanations contained in this work are only the result of counting (increase in the binary number). It is also difficult to accept the resulting determination of all events, including the lack of free will and causality, which we are experiencing so strongly. It would seem that such an important issue as understanding the universe deserves a more sophisticated and complex interpretation involving the most advanced scientific methods (e.g. as in String Theory). However, we tried to explain that extreme simplicity must also apply at the basic or the simplest level. Other reasons also supported this interpretation. An important argument here was the possibility of creating any complex structures (processes, physical objects) by very simple computer programs (which computer theorists pointed out). The second important argument is the fact that simplicity has been achieved here as a result of interdisciplinary association of distant areas of knowledge such as aesthetics, ontology, information theory and physics.

REFERENCES

Arvidsson-Shukur, D.R.M., Barnes, C.H.W. & Gottfries, A.N.O. 2017. Evaluation of counterfactuality in counterfactual communication protocols. *Physical Review A*. doi:10.1103/PhysRevA.96.062316

Berlekamp, E.R., Conway, J.H. & Guy, R.K. 2001. *Winning Ways for Your Mathematical Plays*. Massachusetts: AK Peters Ltd.

Bertalanffy, L. 1968. *General Systems Theory*. New York: G. Brazilier.

Bousso, R. 2002. The holographic principle. *Reviews of Modern Physics* 74: 825–874.

Davies, P. 1993. *The Mind of God: The Scientific Basis for a Rational World*. New York: Simon & Schuster, 14.

Deutsch, D. 2003. Physics, philosophy and quantum technology. In Shapiro, J.H. & Hirota, O. (eds.), The Sixth International Conference on Quantum Communication, Measurement and Computing, *in Proceedings of the Sixth International Conference on Quantum Communication, Measurement and Computing*. Princeton, NJ: Rinton Press.

Hartle, J.B. & Hawking, S.W. 1983. Wave function of the universe. *Physical Review D* 28: 2960–2875.

Jacyna-Onyszkiewicz, Z. 2007. Czy istnieje kres podzielności materii? [Is there a limit to the divisibility of matter?] *Nauka* 3: 105–112.

Joshi, S.T. 2007. *The Agnostic Read*. New York: Prometheus Books, 172–173.

Linde, A. 1986. Eternal chaotic inflation. *Modern Physics Letters A* 1, 2: 81–85.

Lloyd, S. 2006. *Programming the Universe*. New York: Alfred A. Knopf.

Lyre, H. 1995. Quantum theory of ur-objects as a theory of information. *International Journal of Theoretical Physics* 8: 34.

Markopoulou, F. 2012. The computing spacetime. In Cooper, S.B., Dawar, A. & Löwe, B. (eds.), *How the World Computes*. CiE 2012. *Lecture Notes in Computer Science*, Vol. 7318. Berlin: Springer.

Schmidhuber, J. 1997. A computer scientist's view of life, the universe, and everything. *Foundations of Computer Science* 1337: 201–208.

Stanowski, M. 2011. Abstract complexity definition. *Complicity: An International Journal of Complexity and Education* 2: 78–83.

Tatarkiewicz, W. 1981. *Historia Filozofii* [*History of Philosophy*]. Warszawa: PWN, 2, 56.

Tryon, E.P. 1973. Is the universe a vacuum fluctuation? *Nature* 246: 96–397.

Weizsäcker, C.F. 1980. *The Unity of Nature*. New York: Farrar, Straus, and Giroux.

Wolfram, S. 1985. Undecidability and Intractability in theoretical physics. *Physical Review D* 54: 735.

Wolfram, S. 2002. *A New Kind of Science*. Champaign, IL: Wolfram Media INC.

Zuse, K. 1969. *Rechnender Raum*. Braunschweig: F. Vieweg & Sohn.

21 Conclusions

The initial goal of these considerations was to find the reasons for aesthetic preferences and objective beauty criteria. In realizing this goal, the new understanding (or, in fact, clarifying the existing concept) of contrast as the essence of all interactions played a key role. Only such a general principle allowed bringing a new quality to understanding beauty and art. How does the principle of contrast explain these concepts? On the one hand—directly as (strong) tension between the effects of common and differentiating features of (aesthetic) objects, and on the other—indirectly by defining other fundamental concepts related to beauty, such as development, complexity, value, subjectivity, cognition and being.

The principle of contrast as the essence of interactions allows theoretically to analyze anything, because everything we are aware of is a kind of interaction (i.e. being and existence). In these considerations, we tried to show the universality of this principle by analyzing the most diverse objects. We started with comparative analyses of simple abstract visual structures. These analyses allowed an approximate, and in some cases accurate (golden ratio), estimation of the aesthetic value of the objects (both visual and mental).

By analyzing the complex structures of artworks, we have shown on various examples, how artists consciously build contrasts by creating strong relationships between different forms and meanings. Understanding of the essence of beauty and art can be useful for both creativity, making the creative process more conscious, and critical/historical analyses.

The definition of contrast also enabled the analysis of changes in art that have occurred throughout history, starting from the first human drawings to contemporary art.

An important issue that the *Theory and Practice of Contrast* discusses is also the (unexplained yet) reason for the aesthetic attractiveness of colour combinations. It turned out that colours, like other visual objects, can be analyzed and the principle of contrast applies to them.

Aside from the applications of the *Theory and Practice of Contrast* that have been noticed so far, attention should be drawn to its potential for helping to find aesthetic solutions to problems of everyday life. Even though such estimation cannot completely obviate the need for an emotional verification of our judgements, it can help and enable us to engage with greater awareness with the world of aesthetic objects.

Especially important in these considerations was understanding the contrast as the nature of all interactions at the binary level, i.e. at the most fundamental level of existence/perception of reality, and to use binary models in the analysis of the issues under consideration. It allowed an essential understanding (essential, because the binary level is also the limit of our understanding) of all concepts/issues defined in this study through the concept of contrast, which include *interaction, being, development, complexity, information, beauty, art, value, cognition, perception, subjectivity/objectivity, emergence and consciousness.* We see that these concepts (defined through contrast) belong to many different fields of knowledge, both humanistic and natural.

It was also interesting to use the definition of contrast and complexity in solving fundamental problems of artificial intelligence, i.e. the possibility of introducing self-awareness and creativity into it. The conclusions of the analyses not only explain these issues, but also create the opportunity to use them in practice.

An integral part of the whole concept was *Binary Model of Universe*, in which we proposed the model of universe as one of the possible hypotheses, based on *Abstract Complexity Definition*, the *Binary Model of Visual Interactions* and de Broglie's theory. Here too, distant fields are connected, including epistemology, ontology, information theory and physics.

Since Theory and Practice of Contrast is a coherent structure, which for better understanding, would be best to see in its entirety, we present a diagram of connections between its key concepts/issues and a brief description of these connections (Figure 21.1).

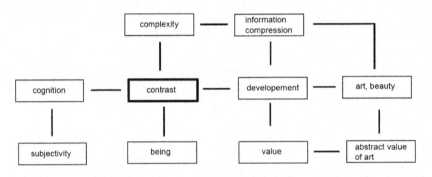

FIGURE 21.1 An integrated system of concepts representing particular fields of knowledge in *Theory and Practice of Contrast*.

Contrast—development: when observing a contrast, we also observe the connection between contrasting objects/structures (resulting from their common features) and the emergence of a new, more complex structure possessing the common and differentiating features of connected structures. In the general sense, the emergence of a new structure is tantamount to development. Therefore, it may be stated that contrast is a perception of structures connections or the experience of development (development of our imagination in this case). The association of contrast with development brings a new quality to the understanding of many other fundamental meanings, such as beauty, value, creativity and emergence. (Similarly, *contrast as development* is understood in Whitehead's philosophy.)

Contrast—complexity: in accordance with the proposed definition, when we consider the contrast between two or more visual objects/structures, it grows in intensity as the number/strength of differentiating and common features of contrasting structures/objects increases. Such an understanding of contrast remains an intuitive criterion of complexity that can be formulated as follows: *a system becomes more complex when the number of distinguishable elements and the number of connections are greater among them.* If in definition of contrast we substitute differentiating features for distinguishable elements and common features for connections, we will be able to conclude that contrast is the perception and measure of complexity.

Note: two types of contrasts can be distinguished—the sensual (physical) contrast, which is determined only by the force of features of contrasting objects, and the mental (abstract), contrast which depends primarily on the number of these features (this contrast can be equated with complexity).

(The equation of contrast with complexity is an important finding for investigations in cognitive sciences, psychology, ontology, epistemology, aesthetics, axiology, biology, information theory, complexity theory and, indirectly, physics.)

Complexity—information compression: intuition says that the more complex object with the same number of components (e.g. words) has more features/information (i.e. more common and differentiating features), which proves its better organization (assuming that all components have the same or similar complexity). We can also say that such an object has a higher degree of complexity. The degree of complexity is in other words the brevity of the form or the compression of information. Complexity understood intuitively (as above) depends, however, not only on the complexity degree (that could be defined as the ratio of the number of features to the number of components) but also on the (total) number of features, because it is more difficult to organize a larger number of elements/features. In addition, the more features (with the same degree of complexity) the greater the contrast. Therefore, in the proposed *Abstract Definition of Complexity*, we multiply the degree of complexity by the number of features. This definition defines the complexity (C) of the binary structure (general model of all structures/objects) as the quotient of the square of features number (N) (which are the regularities/substructures) to the number of components or the number of zeros and ones (n). It is expressed in a simple formula: $C = N^2/n$ and should be considered the most general definition of complexity, among the existing ones, which also fulfils the intuitive criterion. (This relation explains what compression of information in general is and what role it plays as a complexity factor. This allows to generalize the notion of information compression and use it not only in computer science, but also in other fields of knowledge, such as aesthetics, axiology, cognitive science, biology, chemistry and physics.)

Information compression—development: when our mind perceives more compressed objects (receiving information), it saves energy. Compression/organization of information reduces energy of perception while maintaining the same amount of information (in case of lossless compression). Thanks to this, perception becomes easier (more economical) and more enjoyable; for example, it can be compared to faster and easier learning and acquiring knowledge (information), which also contributes to our development.

Compression of information as a degree of complexity also affects its size. Complexity, in turn, is a measure of contrast (and vice versa). Contrast, however, is identified with development. Hence, complexity is also development. This sequence of associations is the second way of connecting compression of information with development. Similarly, one can trace all other possibilities of connections in the scheme.

(The association of information compression with development brings a new, explanatory knowledge to many fields including cognitive science, aesthetics, axiology and information theory.)

Development—value: development is the essence of value, because all values (ethical, material, intellectual etc.) contribute to our development which is their common feature. It follows that value is also a contrast, complexity and compression of information because they are synonymous with development.

(The relation explains and defines the notion of value fundamental to axiology.)

Value—abstract value: about all kinds of values (with the exception of aesthetic values), we can say what they are useful for. Only aesthetic values can be said to serve the development or essence of values, values in general or abstract values. This is a property of abstract concepts to express the general idea of something (e.g. the concept of a chair includes all kinds of chairs and not a specific one). It follows that what is specific to aesthetic value is that it is an abstract value (although it is difficult to imagine).

(This is a new understanding of aesthetic value, crucial for aesthetics and axiology.)

Contrast—being: contrast or interaction is a concept prior to the concept of being, because without interaction, there is no existence. It follows that the basic component of being must be two objects/elements/components (creating a contrast) having common and differentiating features.

(Understanding of being as a contrast is fundamental to ontology and metaphysics and worth considering in physics.)

Contrast—cognition: the object of cognition and the subject (mind) participate in the cognitive process. The object and the subject have common and differentiating features, thus they create a contrast. Cognition consists in attaching (through common features) differentiating features of the object by the subject. In this way, through the contrast, the subject develops. It can therefore be said that cognition is a contrast of the object with the subject.

(This is a new definition of cognition important for epistemology and cognitive science.)

Cognition—subjectivity: the above understanding of cognition agrees to all disputable issues (present, among others, in psychology, cognitive science and aesthetics) regarding the objectivity and the subjectivity of assessments (e.g. whether the source of beauty is the observer's mind or whether it is a specific quality from the observer independent), because it shows that they depend on both the subject and the object, i.e. depend on their relationship—contrast.

Compression of information—beauty: beautiful are objects with high information compression (a large degree of complexity/organization). Thanks to the compression of information, by perceiving beauty, we save energy; the perception becomes more economical and pleasant which favours our development and is therefore a value for us.

(This explains the previously unknown reasons for aesthetic preferences, key to aesthetics, art theory, psychology, cognitive science and neuroaesthetics.)

Development—beauty: beauty contributes to development thanks to the economy of perception. Perception of beauty is accompanied by a sense of development or ease and the pleasure of perception. (This explains the causes of aesthetic preferences.)

Abstract value—beauty and art: only beauty and art have no specific value but they express/have value in general (an abstract value). The objects that make up a work of art are not important, but their contrast-interaction, which results from the complexity of the artwork. (If we see a single object in the gallery, then the art is in contrast with the context—as in the case of Duchamp's "Urinal" or Malevich's "Black Square".) One can say that beauty and art are distinguished (defined) by two elements: abstract value and a large contrast.

(This is a new and only definition of beauty/art that indicates the distinctive common features of all aesthetic/artistic objects, it is crucial for the theory of art, aesthetics, axiology and epistemology.)

Index

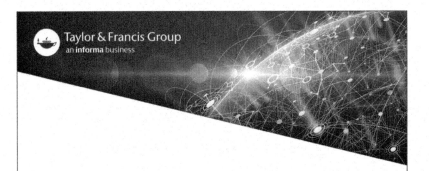